My book of EVERYTHING to COLOR

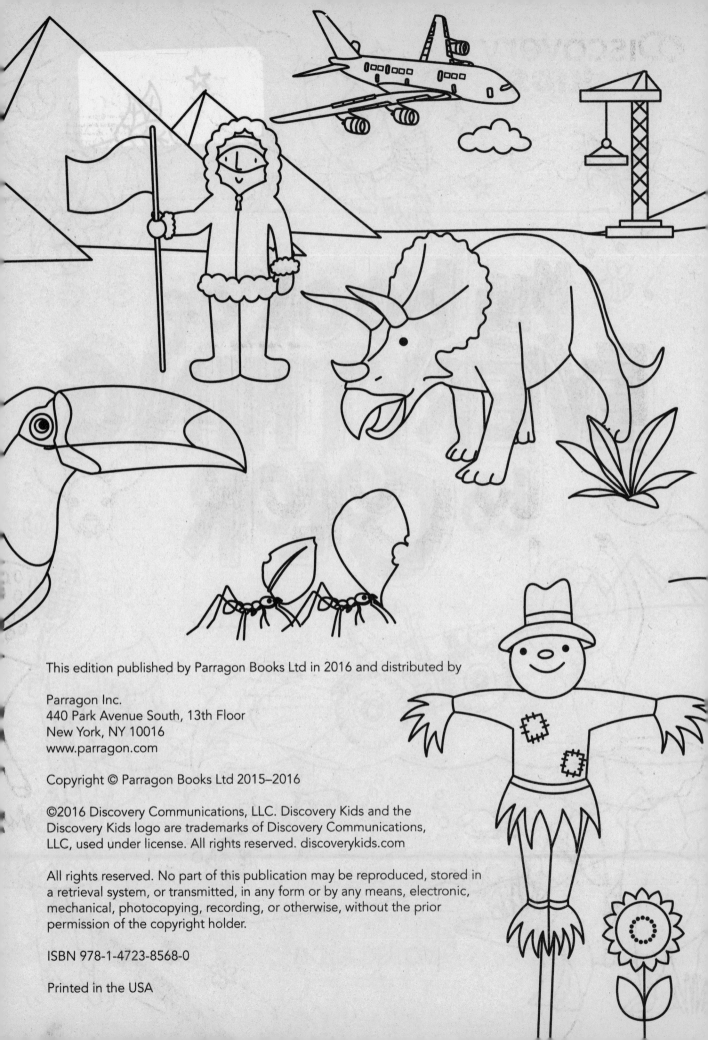

This edition published by Parragon Books Ltd in 2016 and distributed by

Parragon Inc.
440 Park Avenue South, 13th Floor
New York, NY 10016
www.parragon.com

ISBN 978-1-4723-8568-0

Printed in the USA

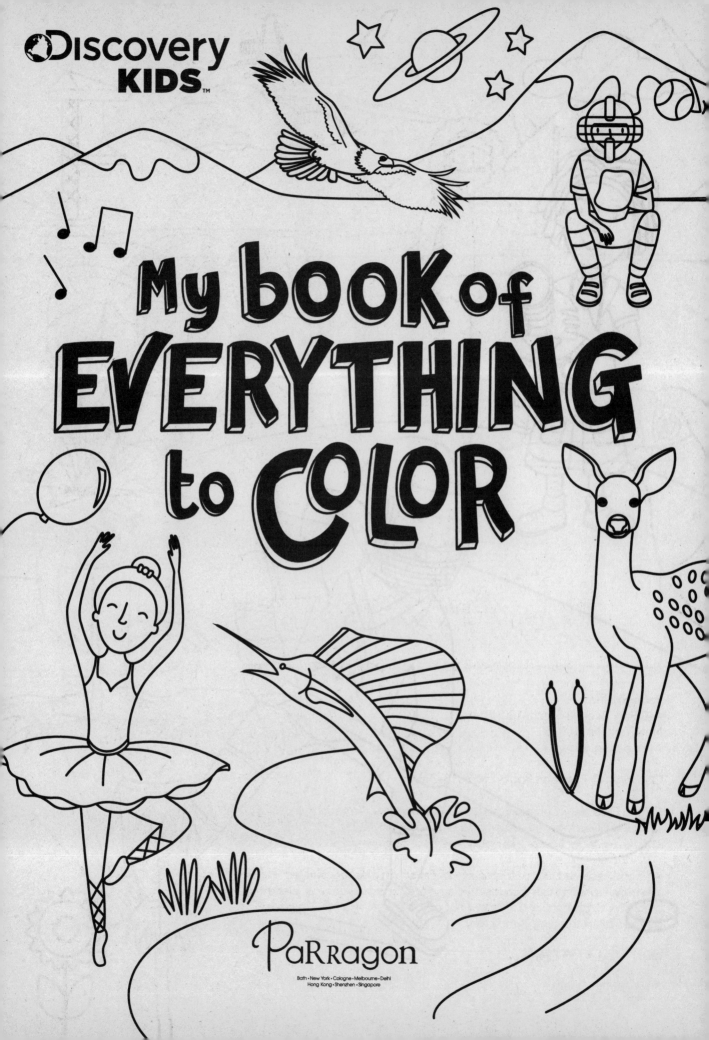

My book of EVERYTHING to COLOR

Discovery KIDS™

PaRragon

Bath · New York · Cologne · Melbourne · Delhi
Hong Kong · Shenzhen · Singapore

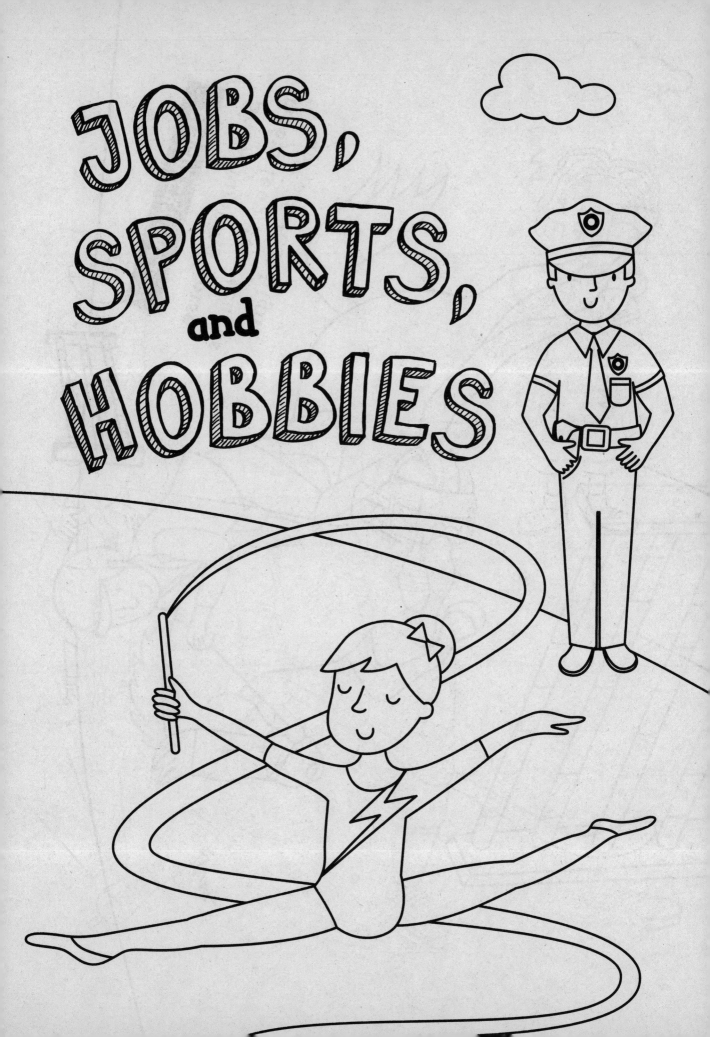

DISCOVERY FACT™

Show jumping horse riders leap over fences up to 5 feet high.

DISCOVERY FACT™

Soccer is the most popular sport in the world.

DISCOVERY FACT™

Some **police officers** work with dogs to track down criminals.

Chef means "leader" in French—leader of the kitchen!

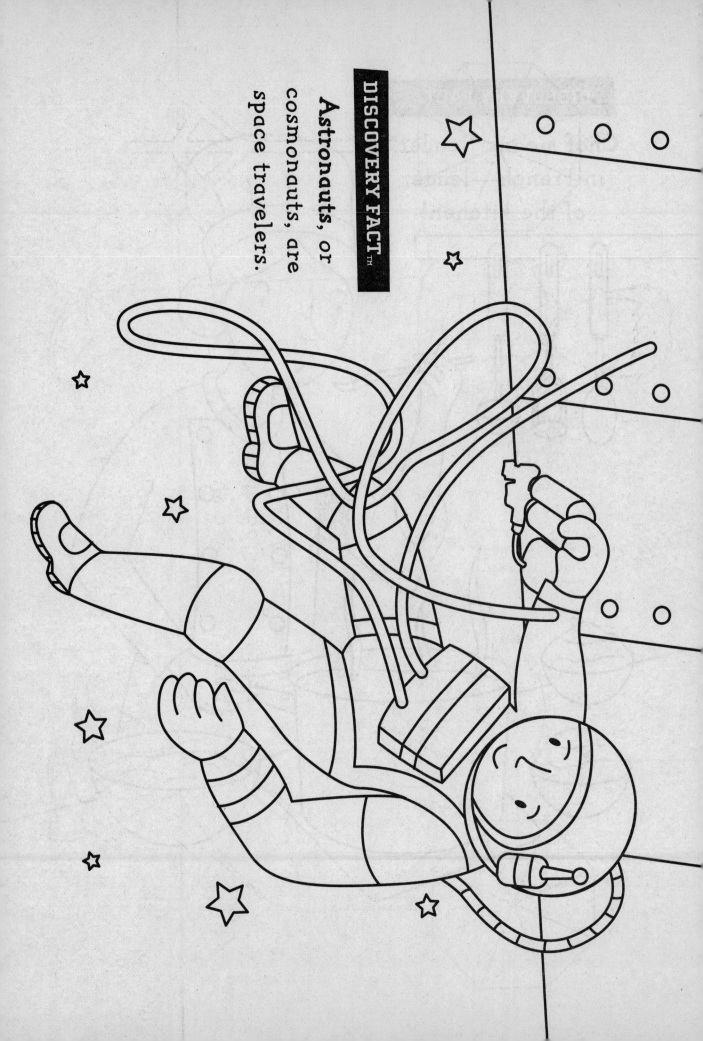

DISCOVERY FACT ™

Astronauts, or cosmonauts, are space travelers.

DISCOVERY FACT™

Photographers can take about 35 photographs a minute during a shoot.

DISCOVERY FACT™

Snowboarders do tricks, such as jumps and twists, as they surf the snow.

Still life **artists** paint objects that don't move.

DISCOVERY FACT™

Veterinarians give medical treatment to sick or injured animals.

DISCOVERY FACT™

Chemists experiment by mixing things together and finding out what happens.

Chess is one of the oldest games
in the world—it was probably
invented over 1,000 years ago!

DISCOVERY FACT™

Softball is the number one team sport in the United States.

DISCOVERY FACT™

Florists' busiest day of the year is February 14— Valentine's Day!

DISCOVERY FACT™

Some **farmers** grow crops, some farmers raise animals, and some do both.

DISCOVERY FACT™

Baseball games can go on for hours, because the game doesn't end until one team wins!

Your hair grows about 6 inches a year—visits to the **hairdresser** or **barber** help keep it neat.

DISCOVERY FACT™

Ice hockey players try to shoot a puck into their opponents' net.

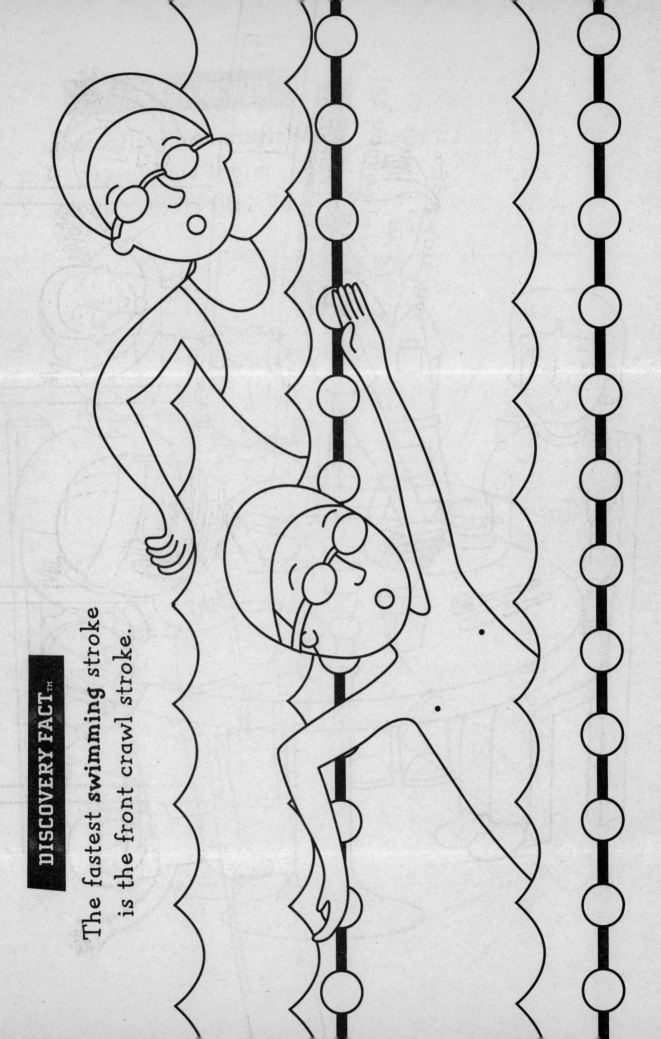

The fastest swimming stroke is the front crawl stroke.

DISCOVERY FACT™

Waiters and **waitresses** might walk over 22,000 steps a day!

Skateboarders use their feet to control the skateboard.

DISCOVERY FACT™

Tall **basketball players** can reach higher and closer to the hoop!

Figure skaters wear boots with blades on the bottom to glide across the ice.

Mechanics use special tools to repair broken-down cars.

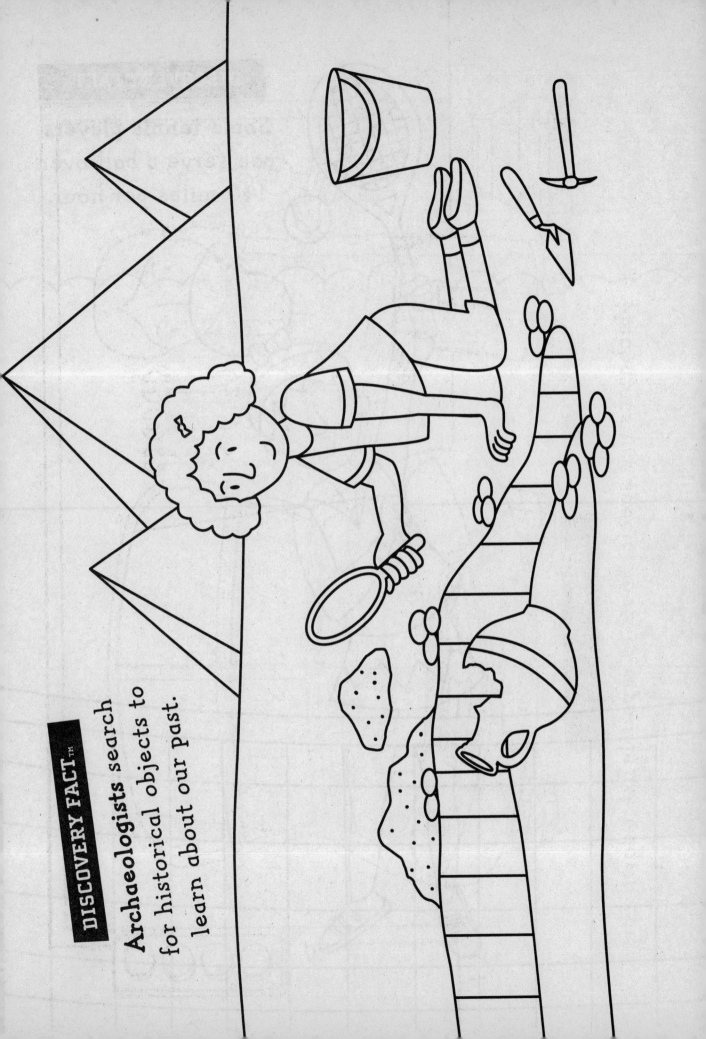

DISCOVERY FACT™

Archaeologists search for historical objects to learn about our past.

DISCOVERY FACT™

Some **tennis players** can serve a ball over 140 miles per hour.

Cycling is a healthy and environmentally friendly way of traveling.

DISCOVERY FACT ™

Many construction workers are builders, plasterers, carpenters, and bricklayers!

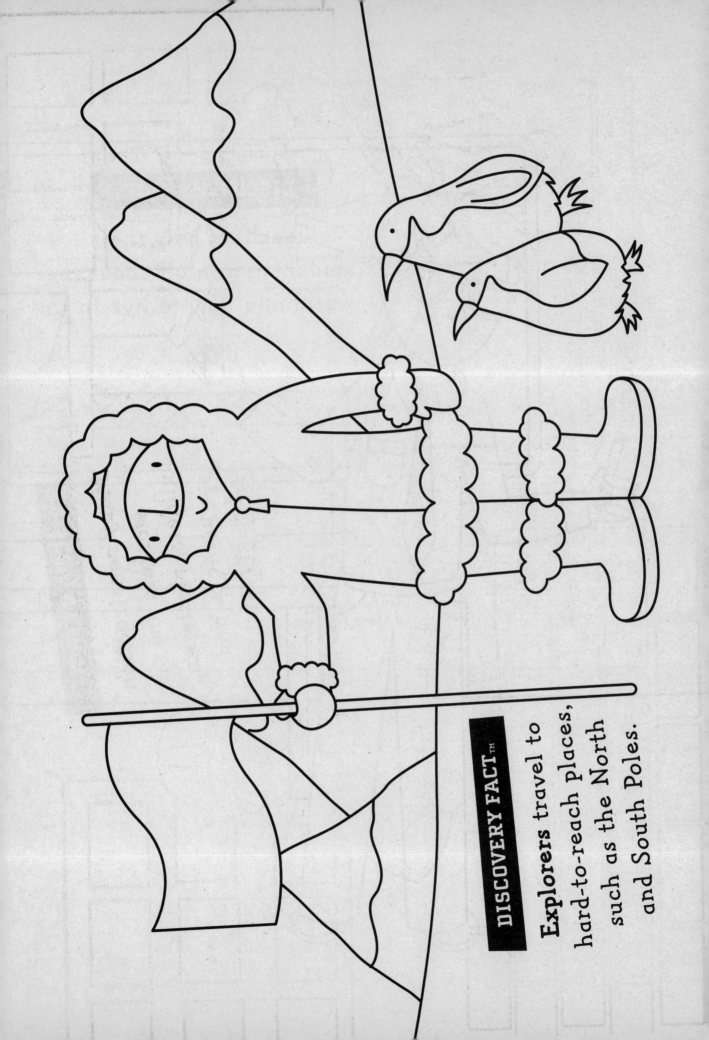

DISCOVERY FACT™

Explorers travel to hard-to-reach places, such as the North and South Poles.

DISCOVERY FACT™

Teachers help their students learn all about the world and how to live in it.

As well as putting out fires, **firefighters** sometimes rescue cats from trees!

DISCOVERY FACT™

Postal workers around the world deliver billions of letters and packages each year!

DISCOVERY FACT™

There are about
38 million **fishermen**
around the world.

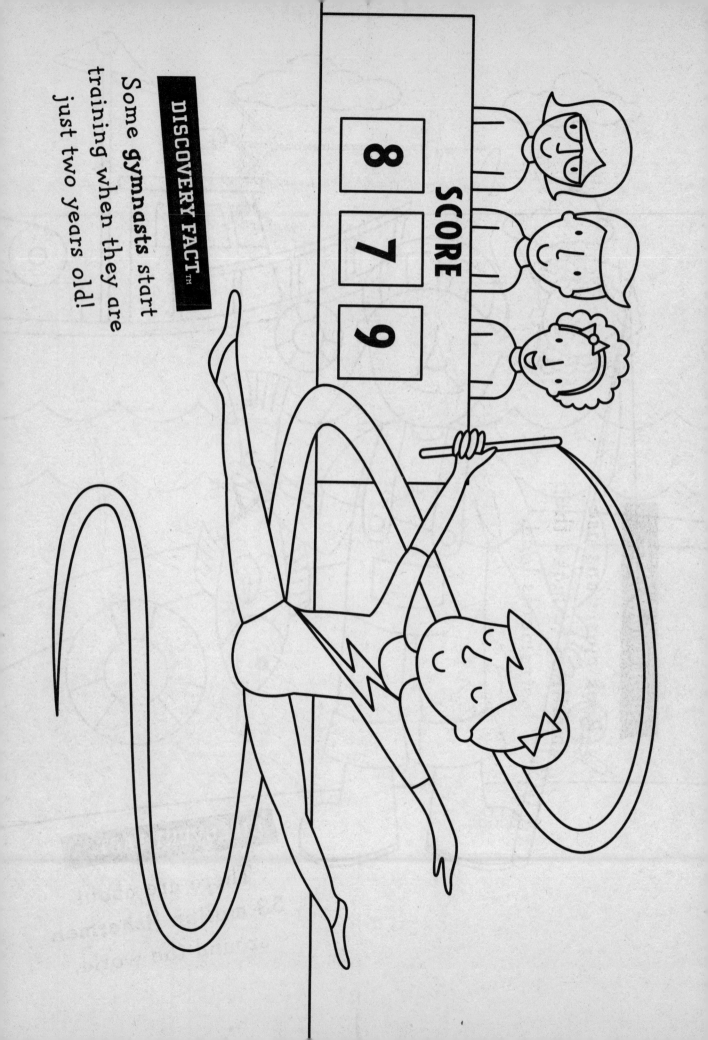

DISCOVERY FACT™

Some gymnasts start training when they are just two years old!

SCORE

8 7 9

Rock musicians use amplifiers to make their instruments loud.

DISCOVERY FACT™

Camping is the number one outdoor vacation activity in the United States.

DISCOVERY FACT™

The sport of volleyball was invented in 1895 in Massachusetts.

Singers use microphones to make their voices loud enough to sing along with other instruments.

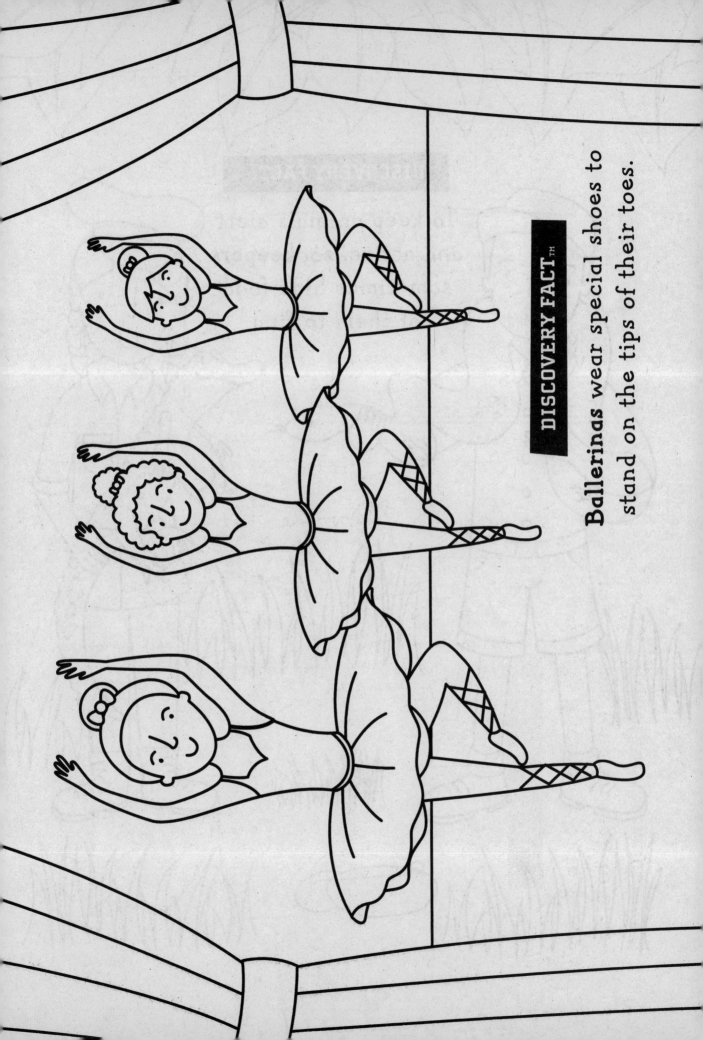

DISCOVERY FACT™

Ballerinas wear special shoes to stand on the tips of their toes.

DISCOVERY FACT™

To keep animals alert and active, **zookeepers** sometimes hide food for them to find.

House painters use rollers and brushes to cover walls with paint.

START

DISCOVERY FACT™

Marathon runners enter
races that are just
over 26 miles long.

The first **golf** balls were
made out of wood.

DISCOVERY FACT™

When clothes were not sold in stores, people got their dresses and suits from **dressmakers** and **tailors**.

DISCOVERY FACT™

Using a skillful kick, **karate experts** can split a plank of wood in two.

There are more than
20,000 **clowns** in the world.

DISCOVERY FACT™

Astronomy is the study of space, including planets, moons, and stars.

Train drivers stop along the railroad track to pick up and drop off passengers.

15

DISCOVERY FACT™

Dancing to music keeps people fit and healthy.

DISCOVERY FACT™

Watching TV is a popular pastime.

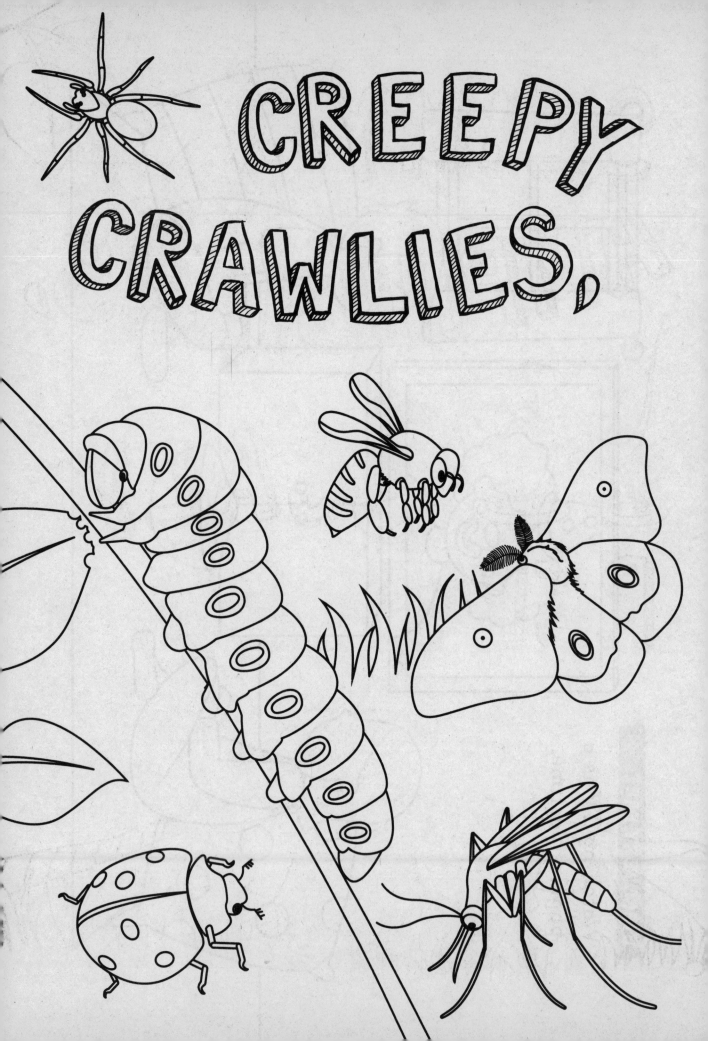

CREEPY CRAWLIES,

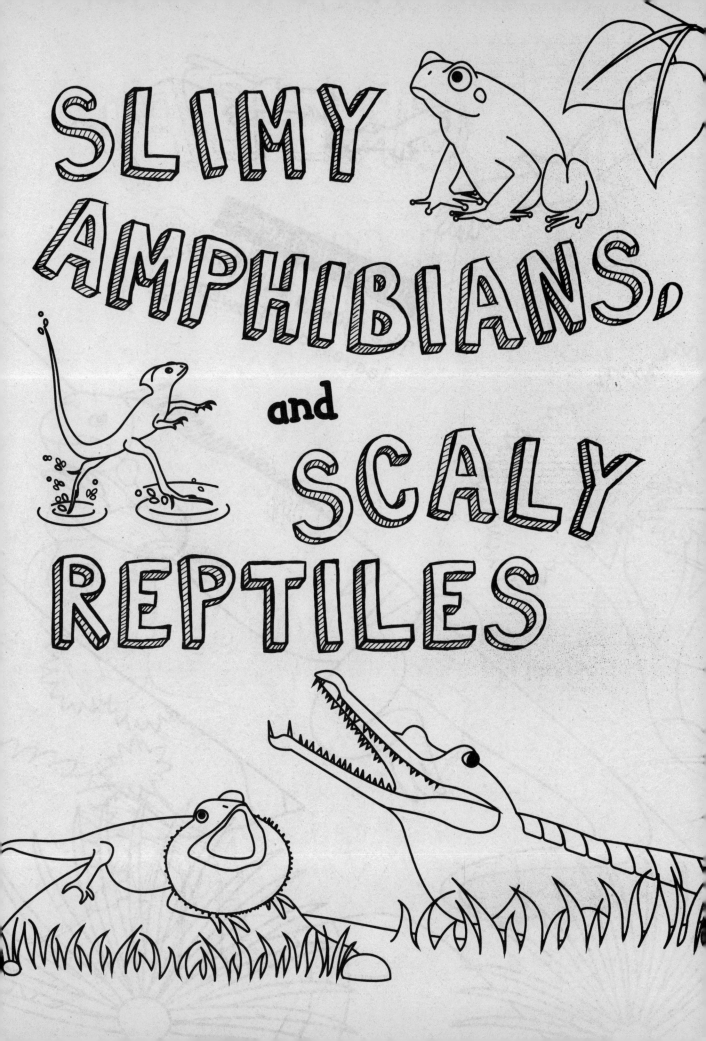

The **iguana** eats fruit, leaves, and flowers.

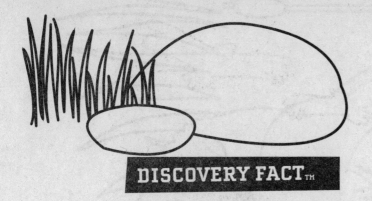

DISCOVERY FACT™

The noise that a **rattesnake's** tail makes warns other animals to stay away!

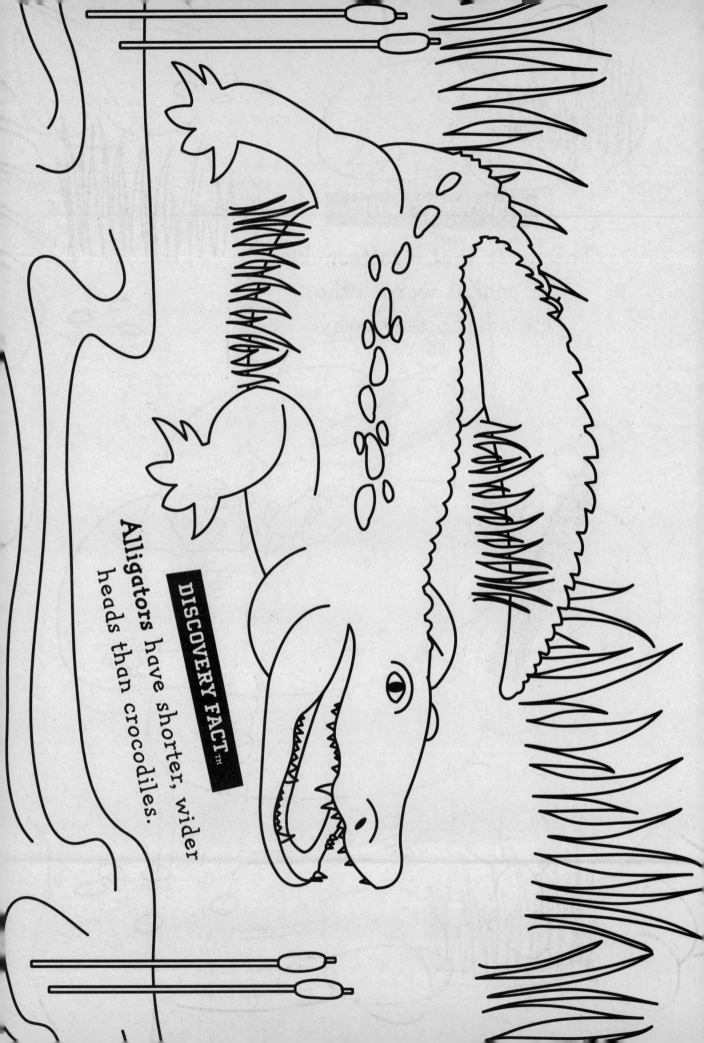

DISCOVERY FACT™

Alligators have shorter, wider heads than crocodiles.

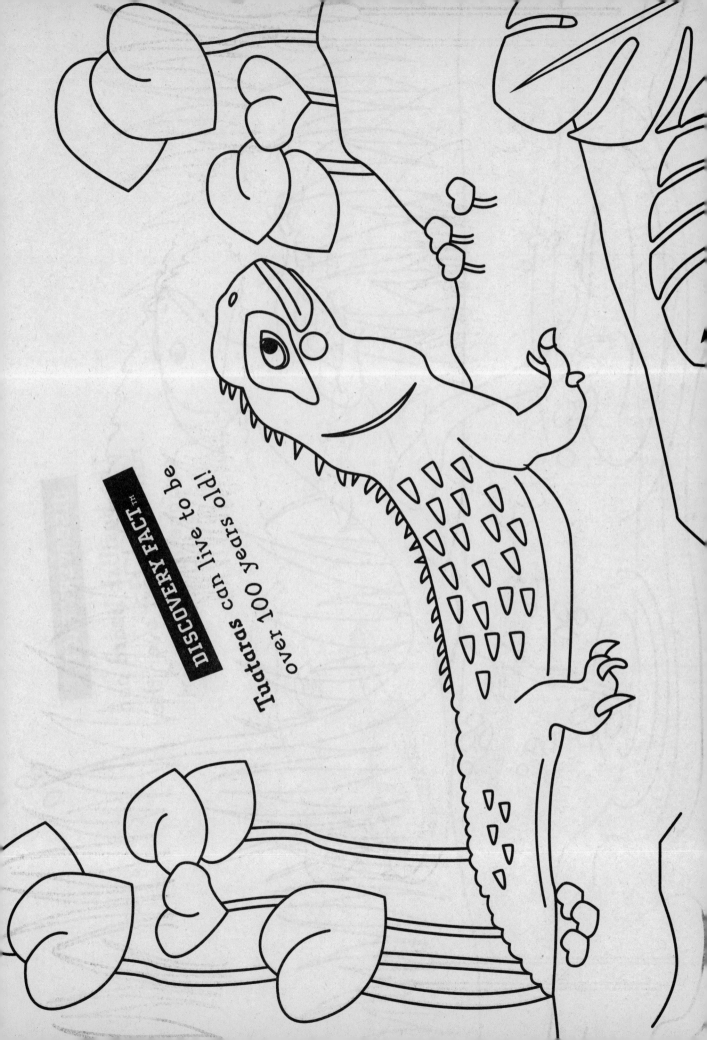

DISCOVERY FACT™

Tuataras can live to be over 100 years old!

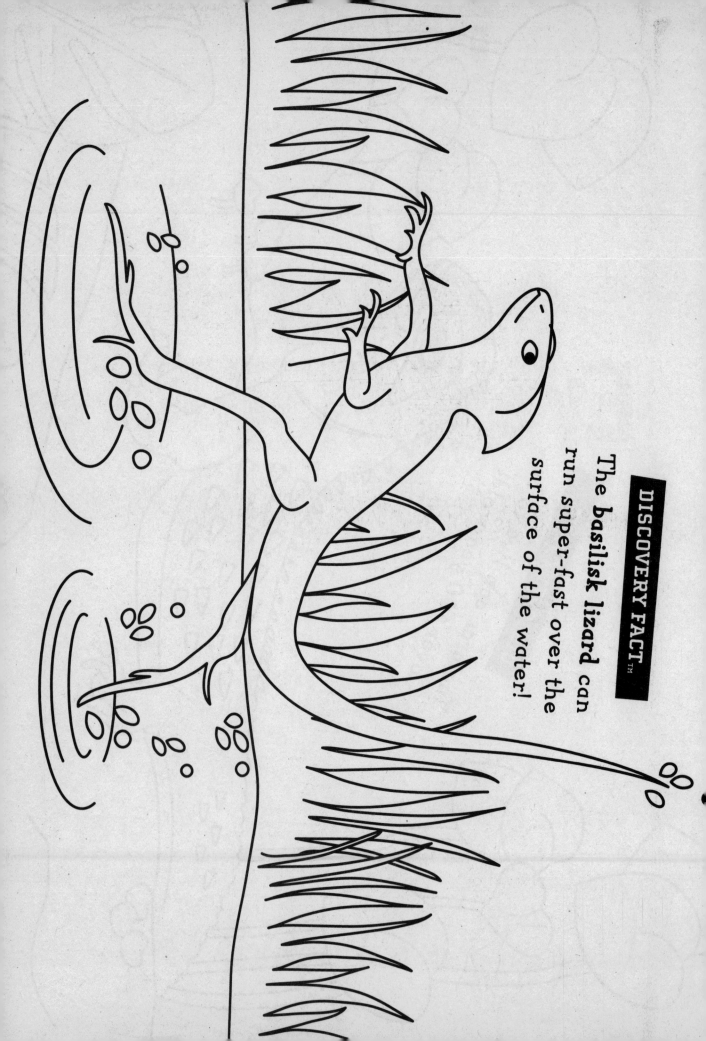

The basilisk lizard can run super-fast over the surface of the water!

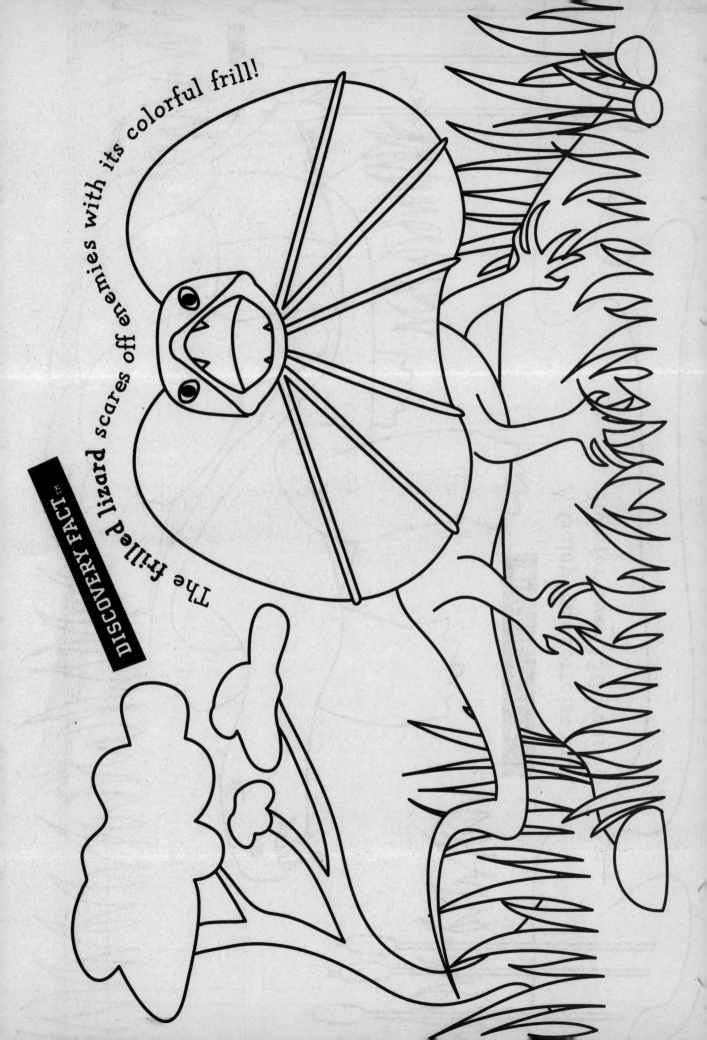

DISCOVERY FACT™

The frilled lizard scares off enemies with its colorful frill!

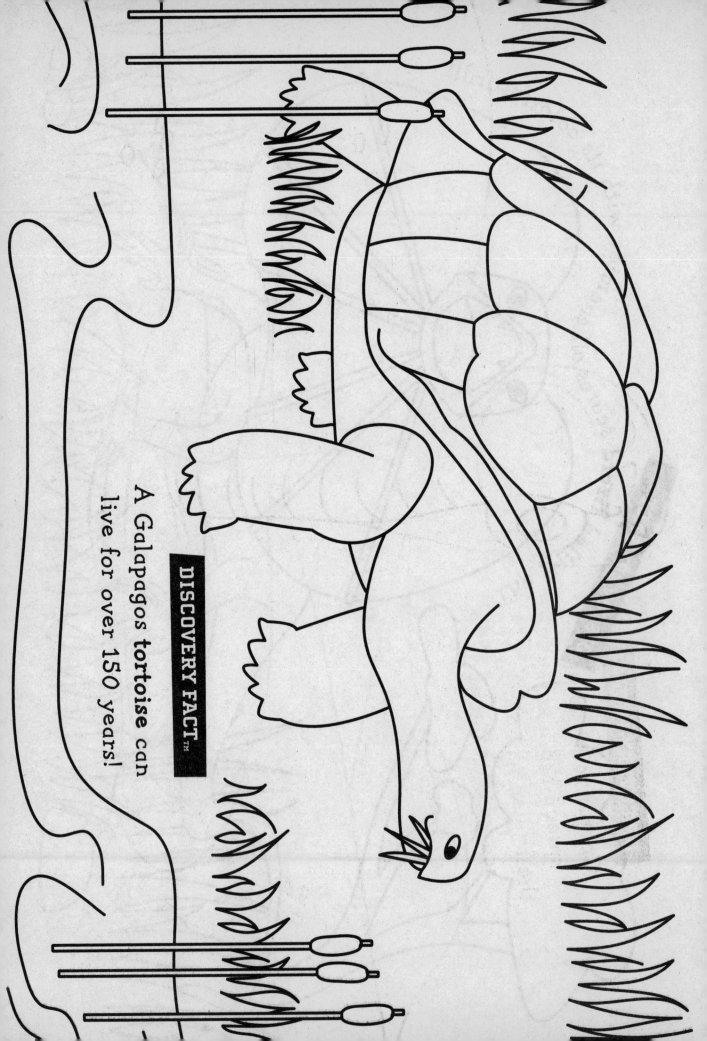

DISCOVERY FACT™

A Galapagos tortoise can live for over 150 years!

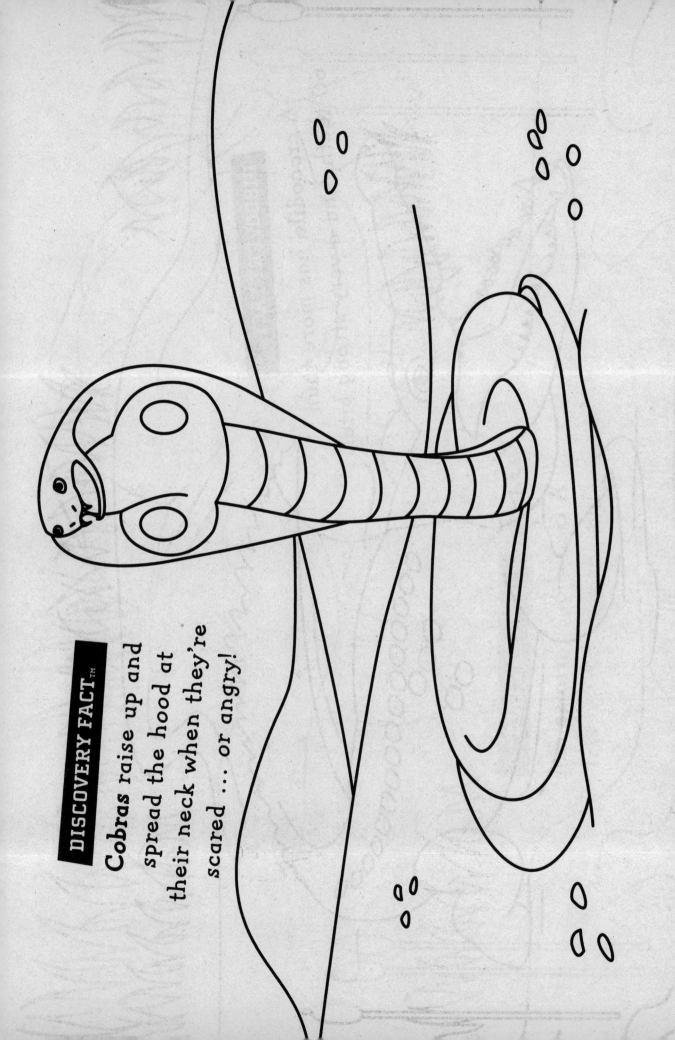

DISCOVERY FACT™

Cobras raise up and spread the hood at their neck when they're scared ... or angry!

A crocodile has more than 60 teeth, and a very strong bite!

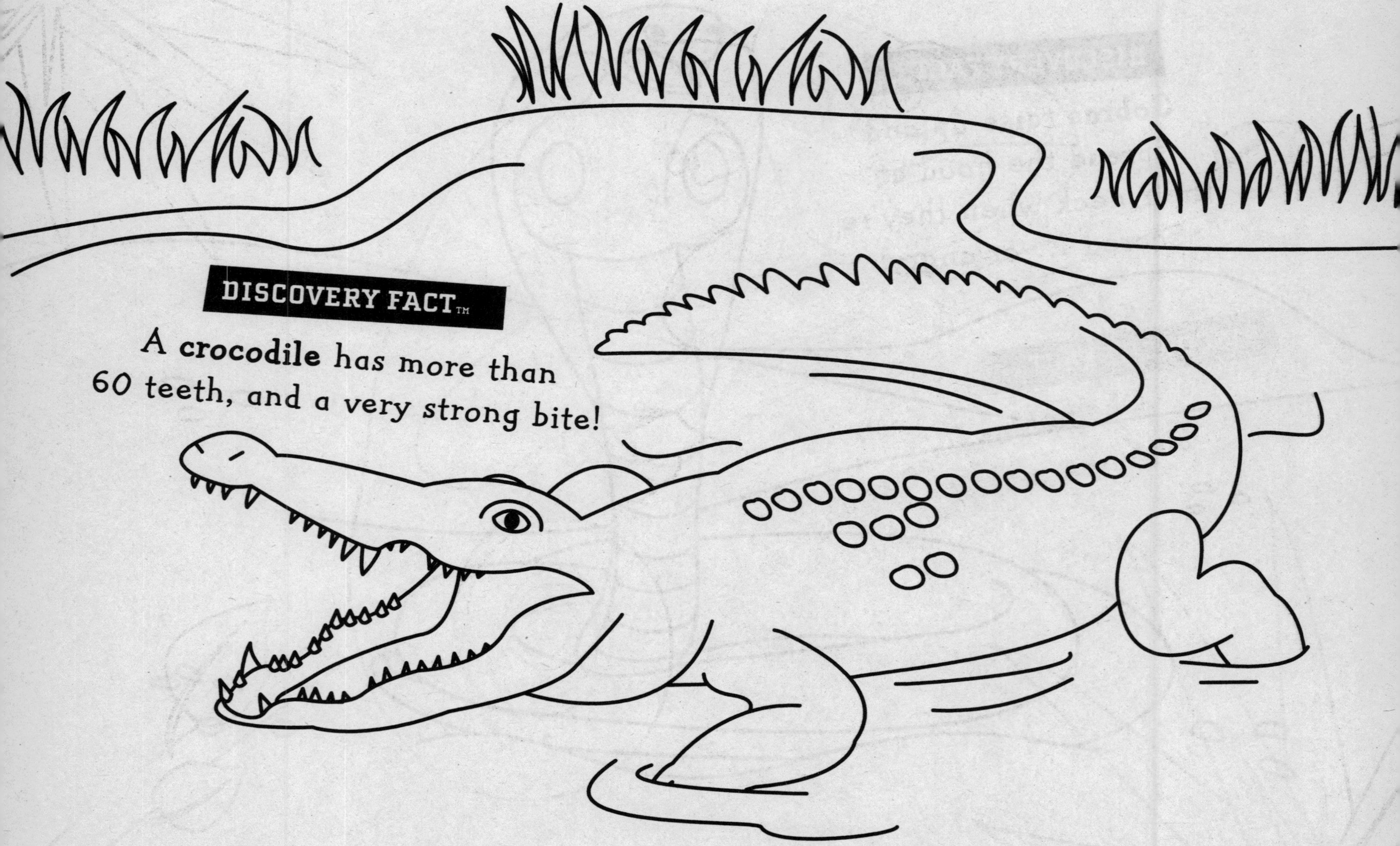

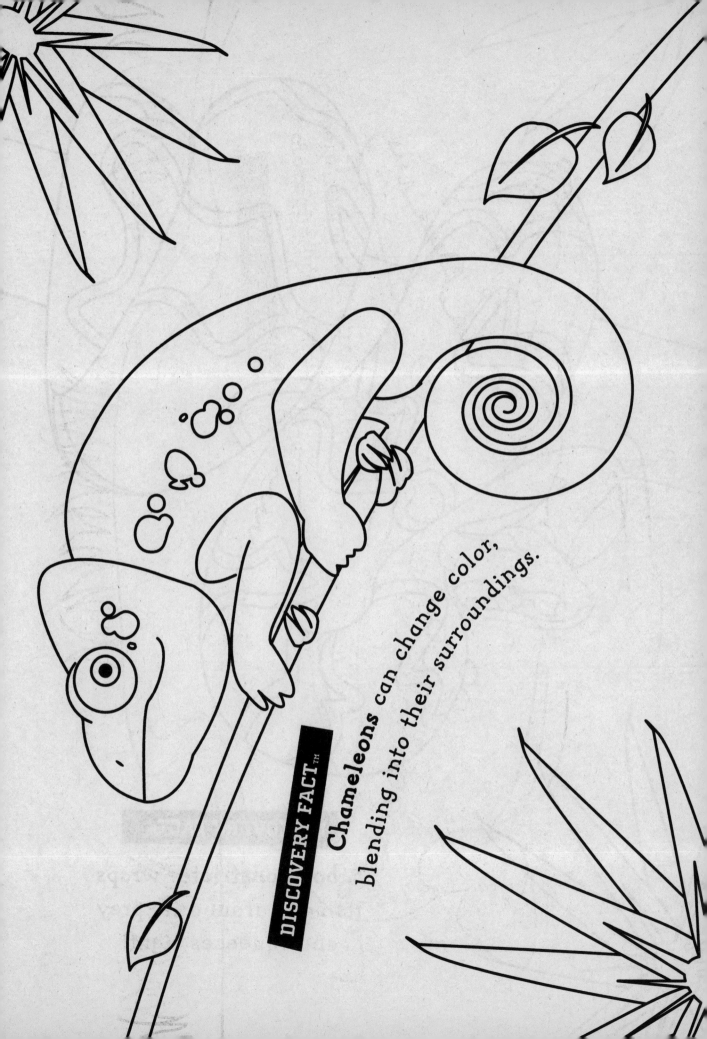

Chameleons can change color, blending into their surroundings.

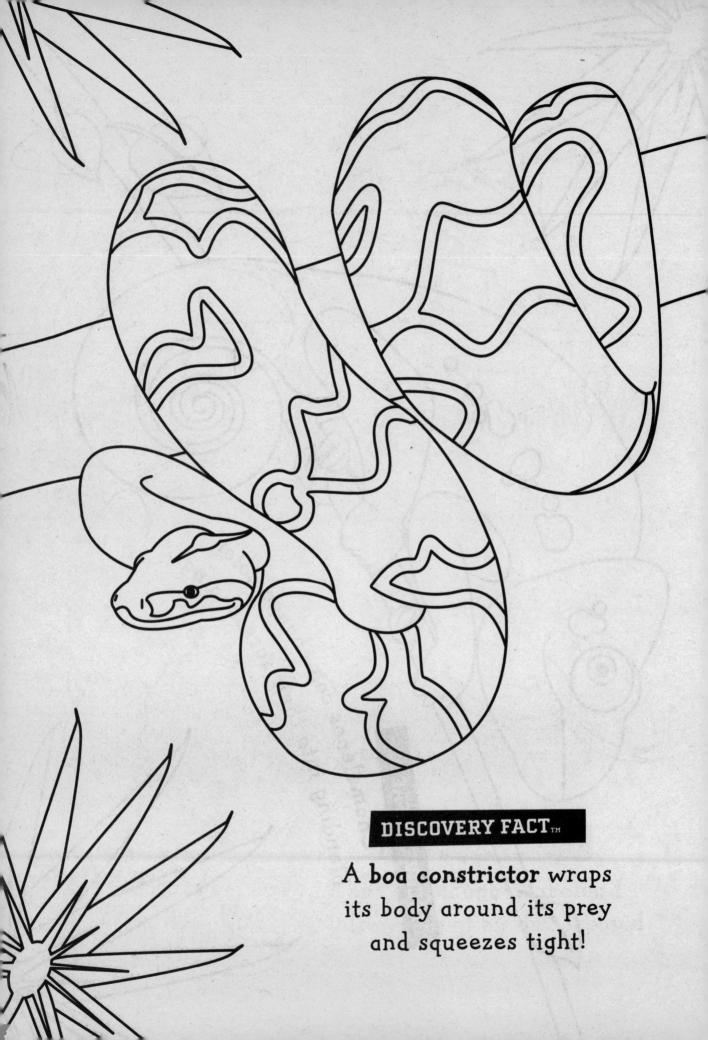

DISCOVERY FACT™

A **boa constrictor** wraps
its body around its prey
and squeezes tight!

DISCOVERY FACT™

Komodo dragons are the
biggest lizards in the world!

DISCOVERY FACT™

A gecko can shed its tail by choice!

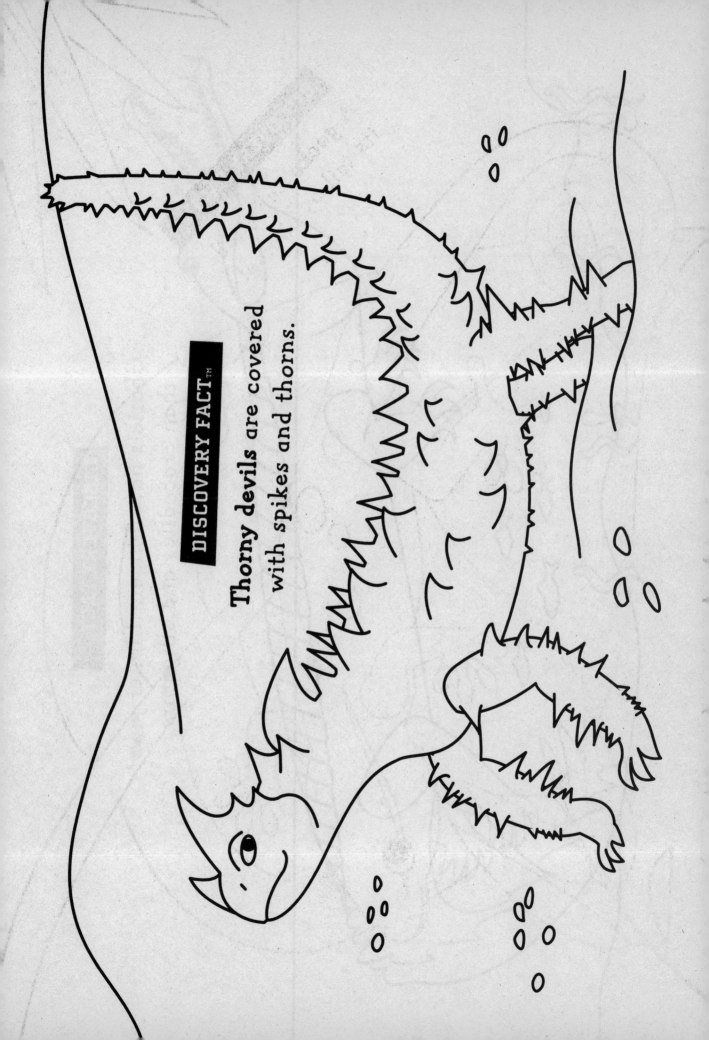

DISCOVERY FACT™

Thorny devils are covered with spikes and thorns.

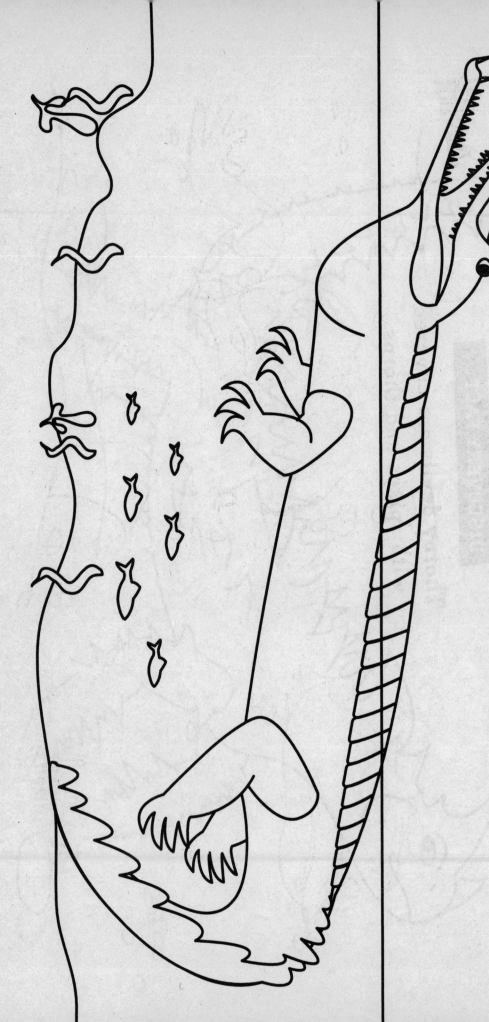

Gharials have longer, thinner jaws than crocodiles and alligators.

The poisonous **Gila monster** only eats 5 to 10 times a year!

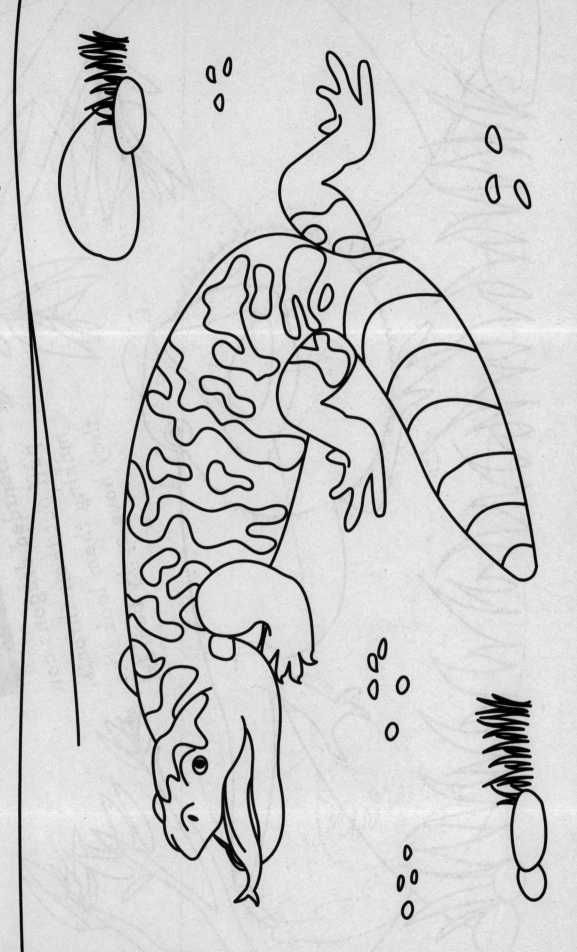

DISCOVERY FACT™

Bearded dragons can puff out their throats, making them look like they have spiky beards!

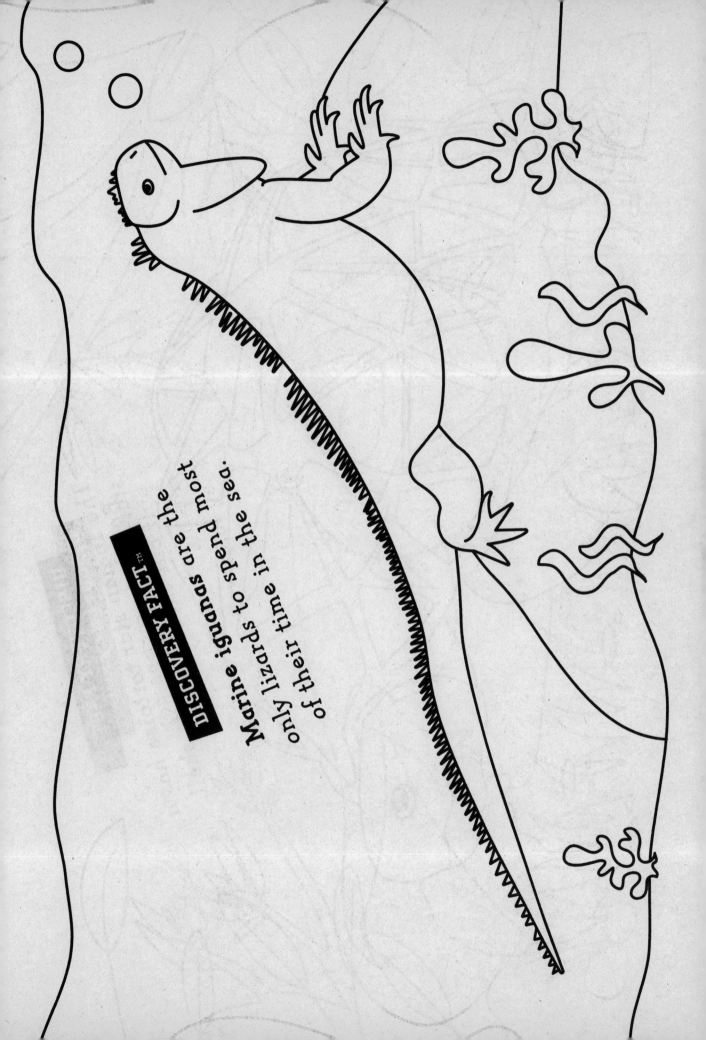

DISCOVERY FACT™

Marine iguanas are the only lizards to spend most of their time in the sea.

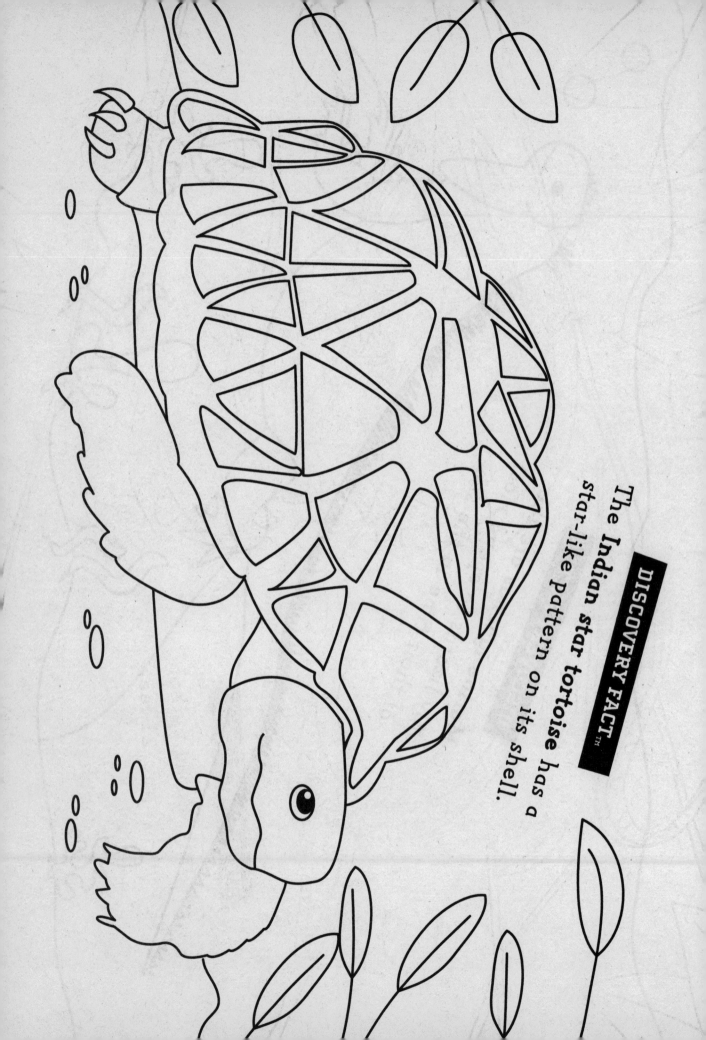

The Indian star tortoise has a star-like pattern on its shell.

DISCOVERY FACT™

The reticulated python can grow up to 21 feet long—half the length of a school bus!

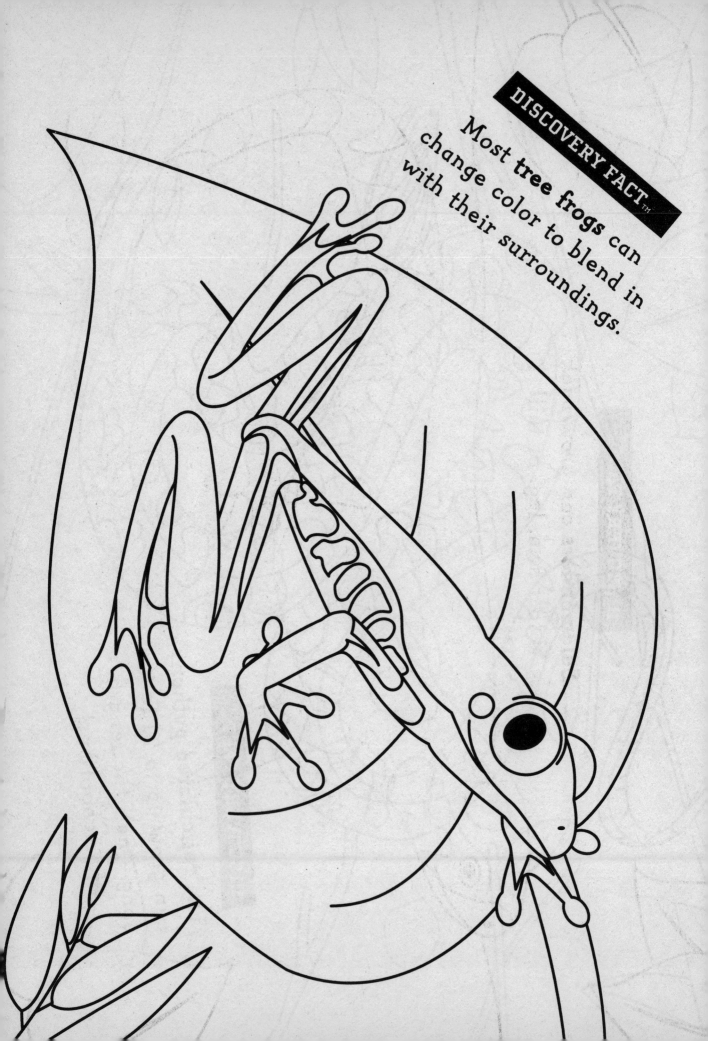

Most tree frogs can change color to blend in with their surroundings.

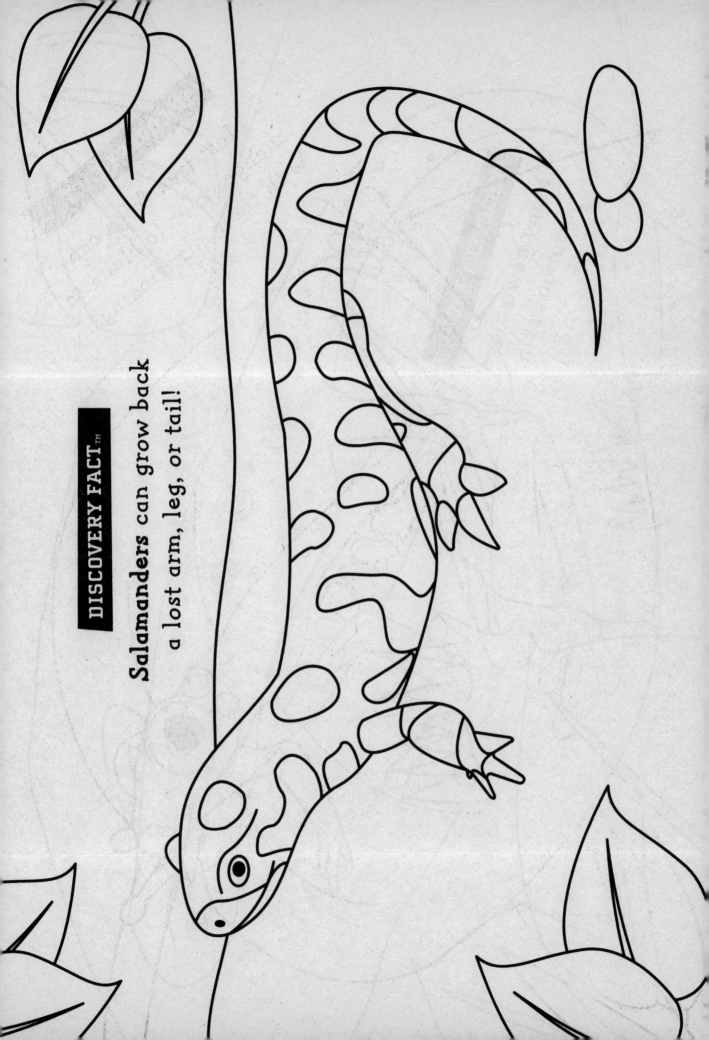

DISCOVERY FACT™

Salamanders can grow back a lost arm, leg, or tail!

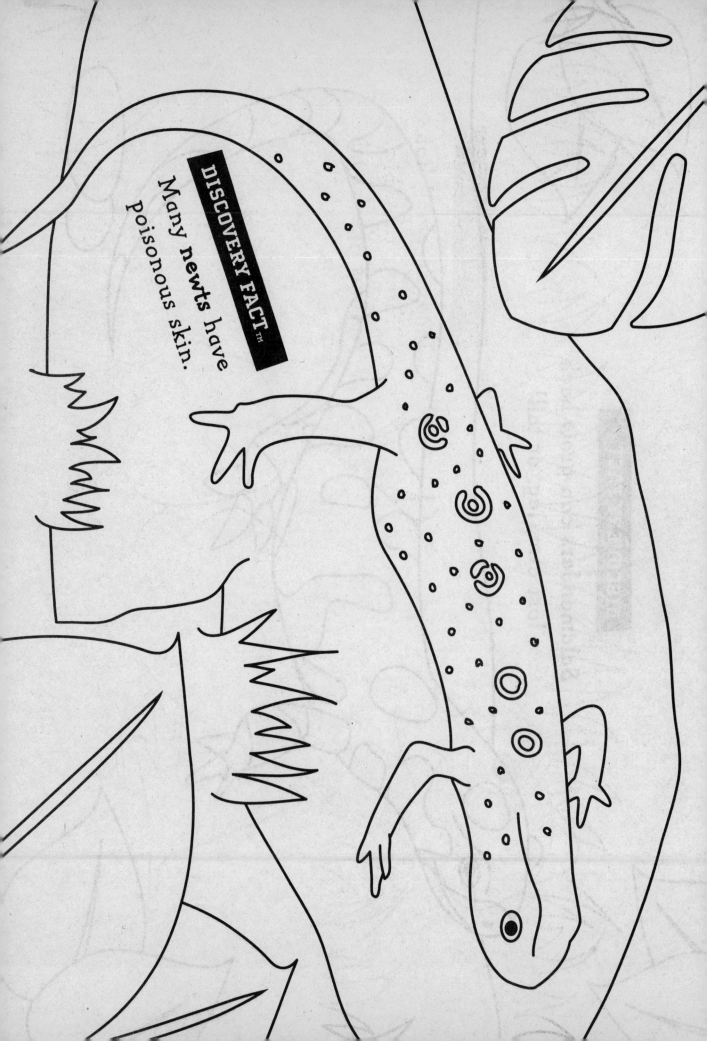

DISCOVERY FACT™

Many **newts** have
poisonous skin.

DISCOVERY FACT™

Toads do small hops rather than big jumps like frogs!

DISCOVERY FACT™

Box turtles are native to the United States and Mexico.

DISCOVERY FACT™

Dwarf caimans are the smallest type of crocodile—at only 4 feet long.

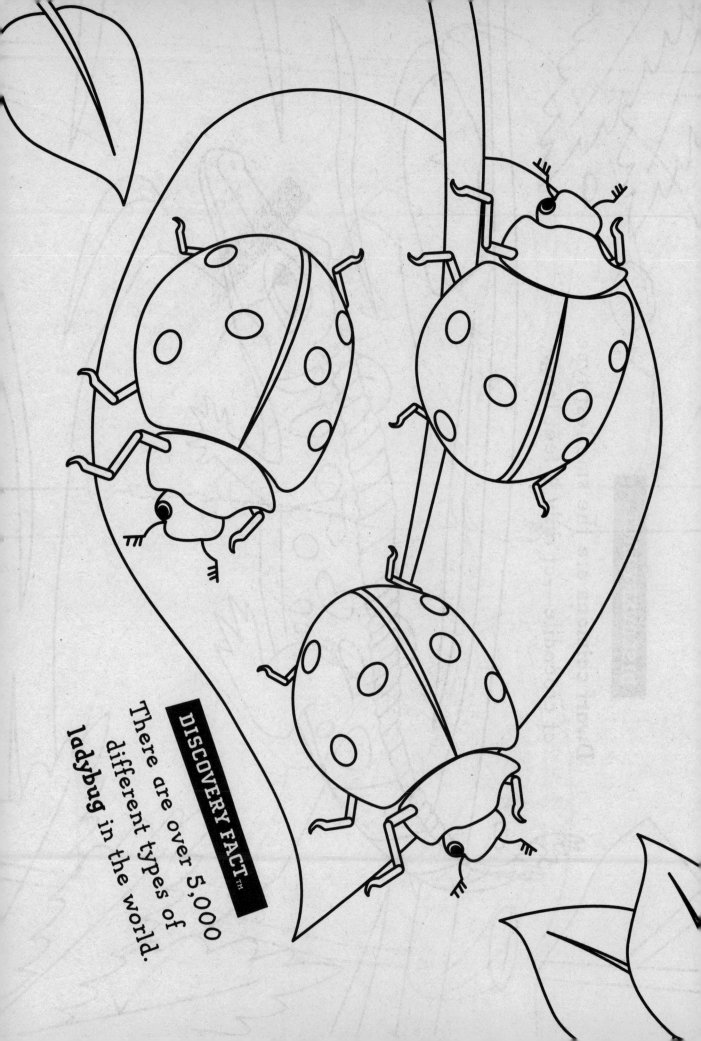

DISCOVERY FACT™

There are over 5,000 different types of ladybug in the world.

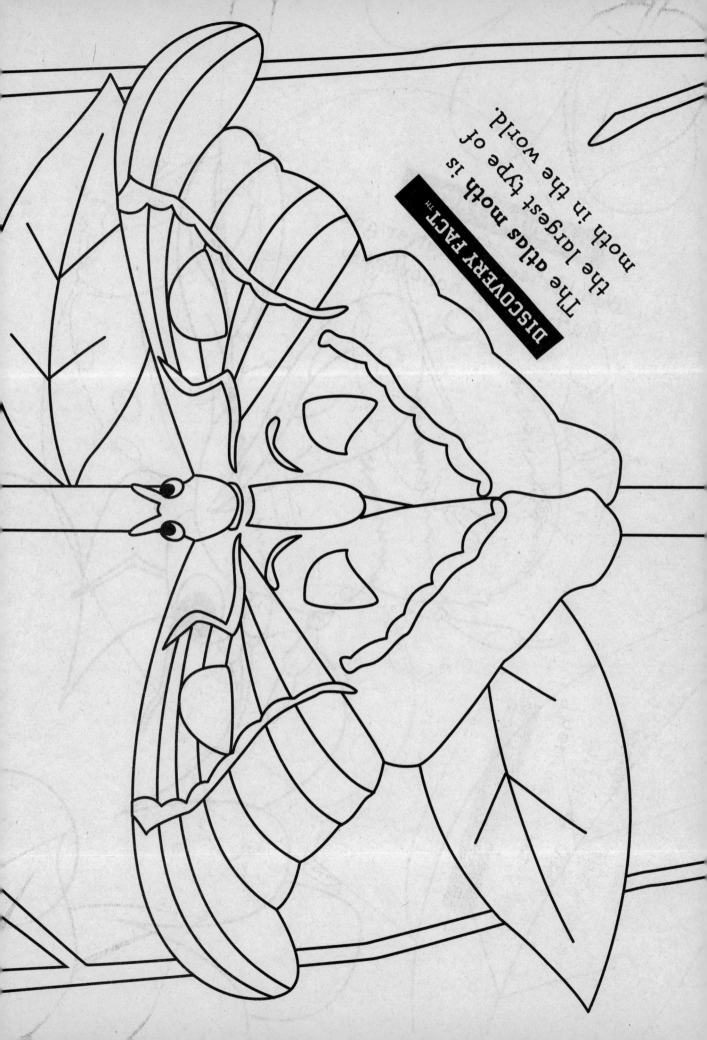

DISCOVERY FACT™

Bumblebees are fatter and fluffier than honeybees.

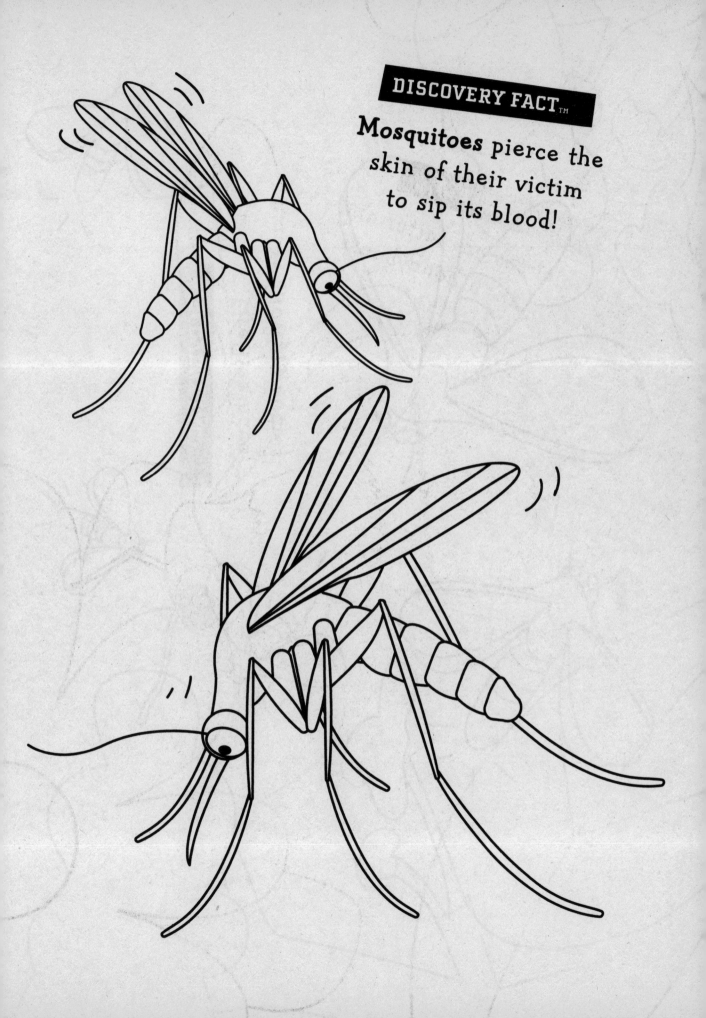

DISCOVERY FACT™

Mosquitoes pierce the skin of their victim to sip its blood!

DISCOVERY FACT™

Fireflies have glowing bodies!

DISCOVERY FACT™

The American lady
butterfly's wings are
orange with black edges.

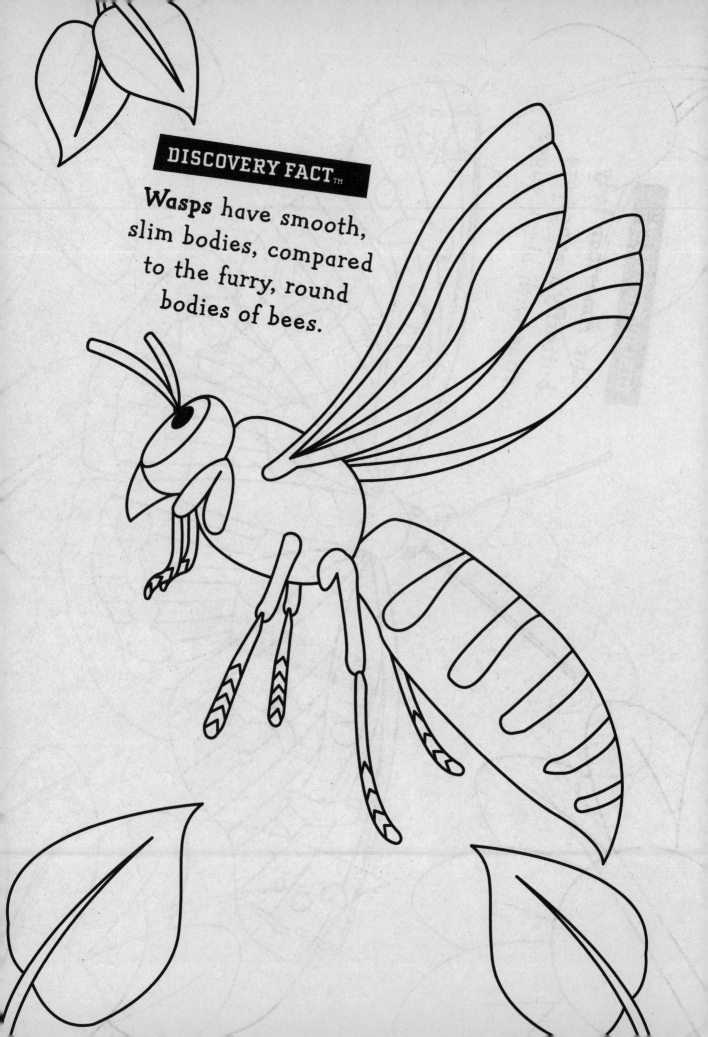

DISCOVERY FACT ™

Wasps have smooth, slim bodies, compared to the furry, round bodies of bees.

DISCOVERY FACT™

Most **caterpillars** have eight pairs of legs!

DISCOVERY FACT™

Monarch butterflies' wings flap slower than other butterflies.

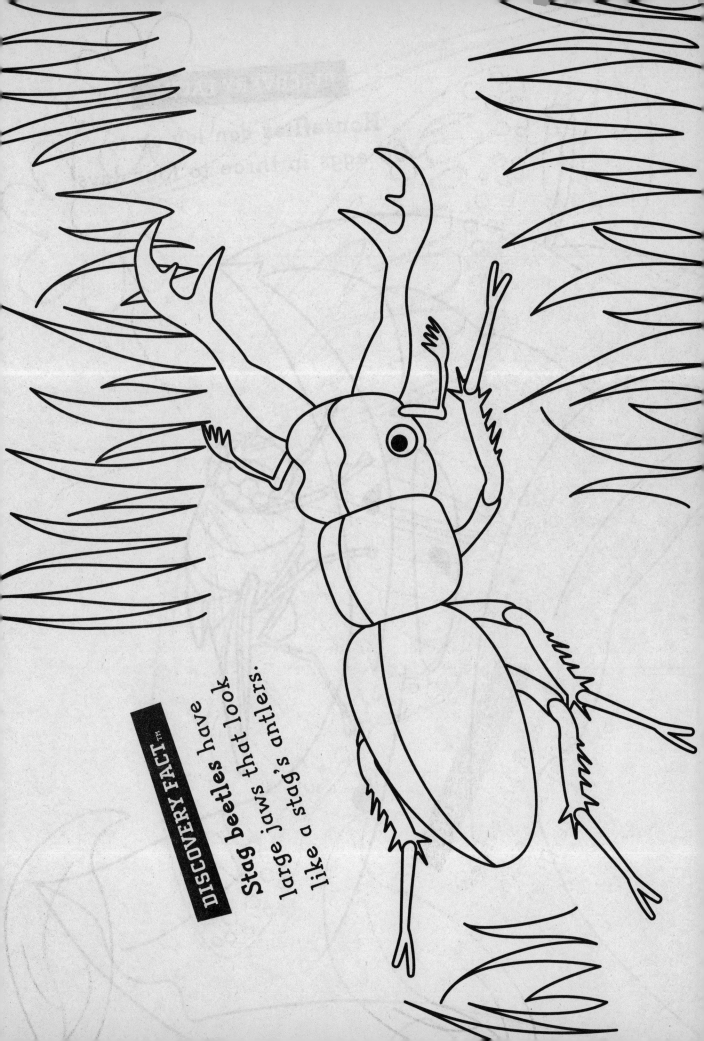

Stag beetles have
large jaws that look
like a stag's antlers.

Houseflies can lay up to 500 eggs in three to four days!

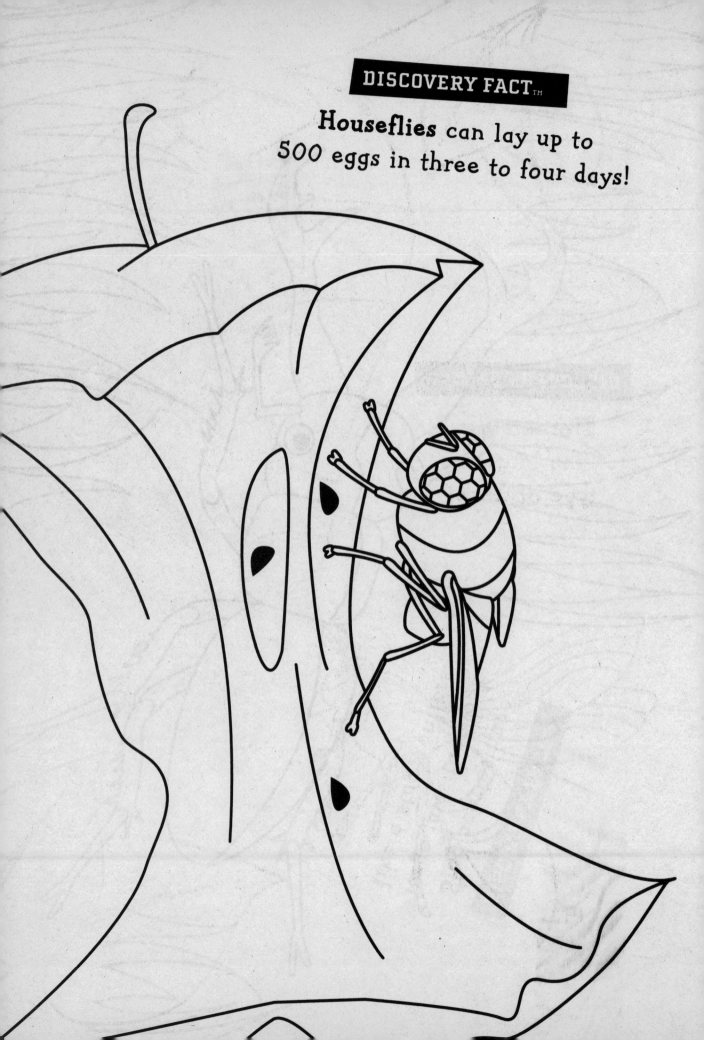

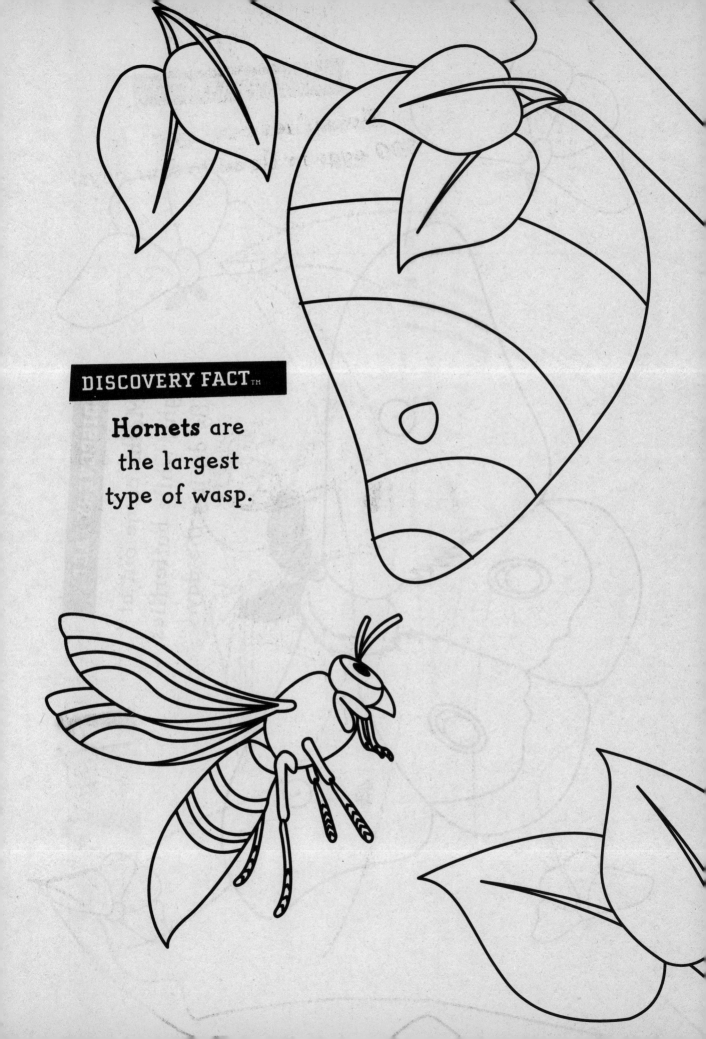

DISCOVERY FACT ™

Hornets are
the largest
type of wasp.

Moths come out at night, while butterflies fly during the day.

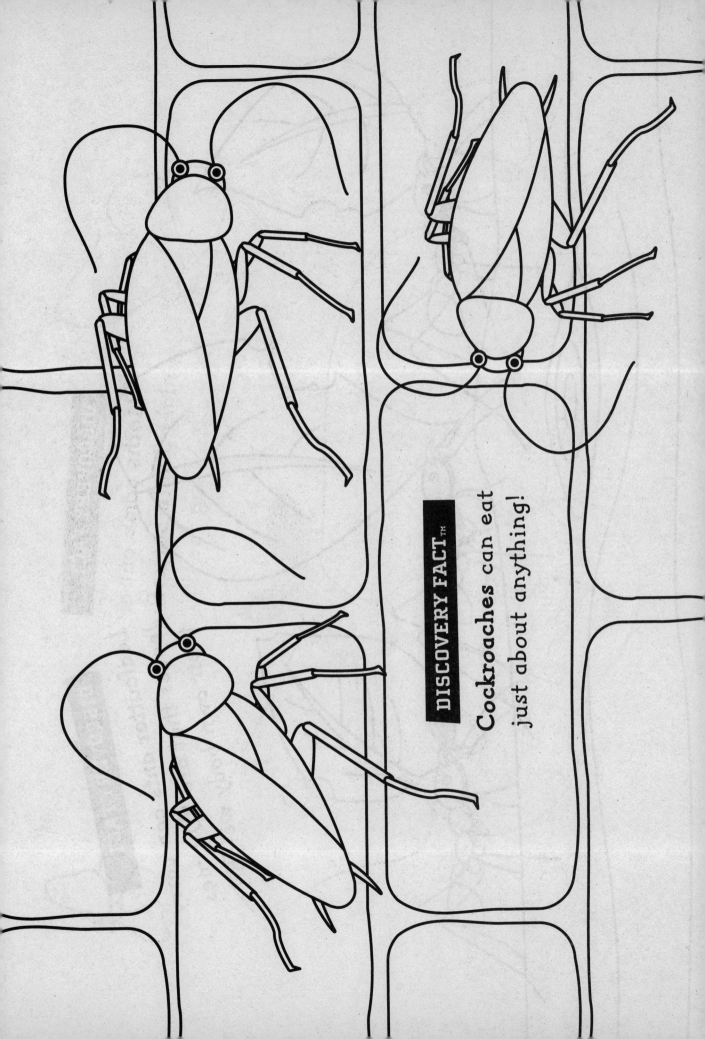

DISCOVERY FACT™

Cockroaches can eat just about anything!

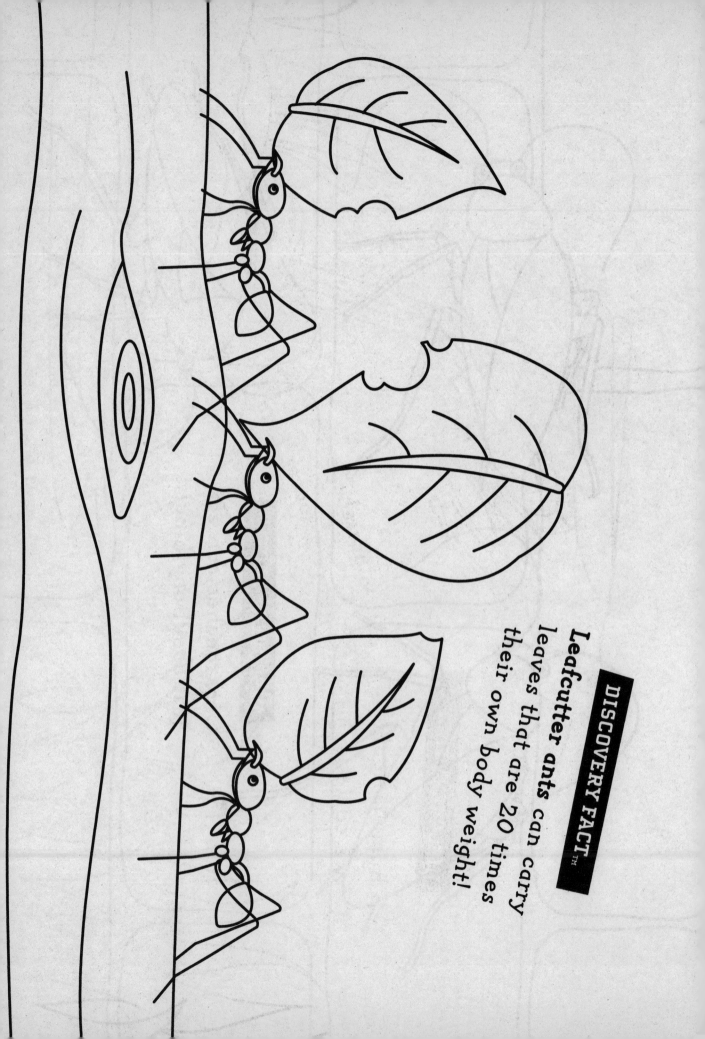

DISCOVERY FACT™

Leafcutter ants can carry leaves that are 20 times their own body weight!

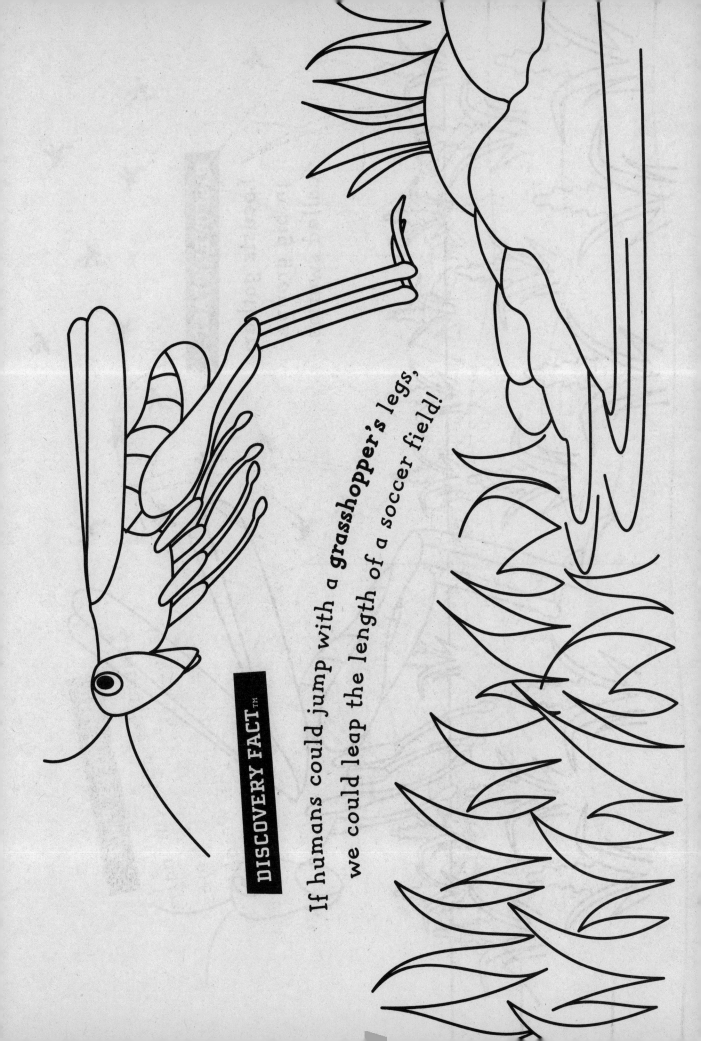

DISCOVERY FACT™

If humans could jump with a **grasshopper's legs,** we could leap the length of a soccer field!

DISCOVERY FACT™

Locusts gather in big groups, called swarms.

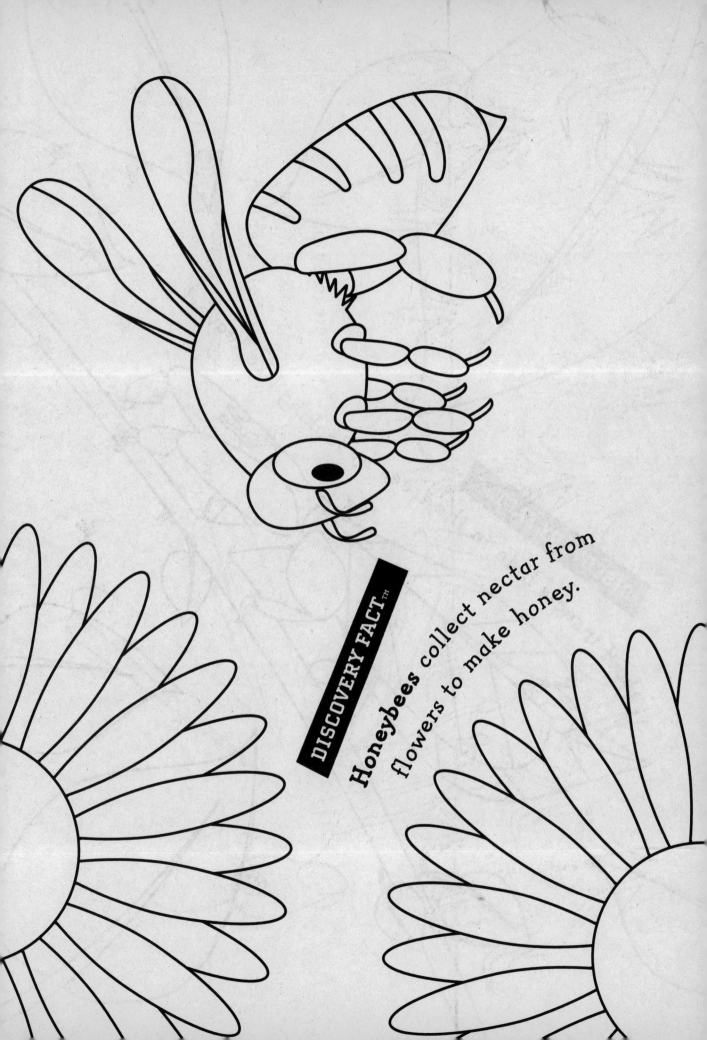

Honeybees collect nectar from flowers to make honey.

DISCOVERY FACT™

Leaf insects hide in the trees by looking like leaves!

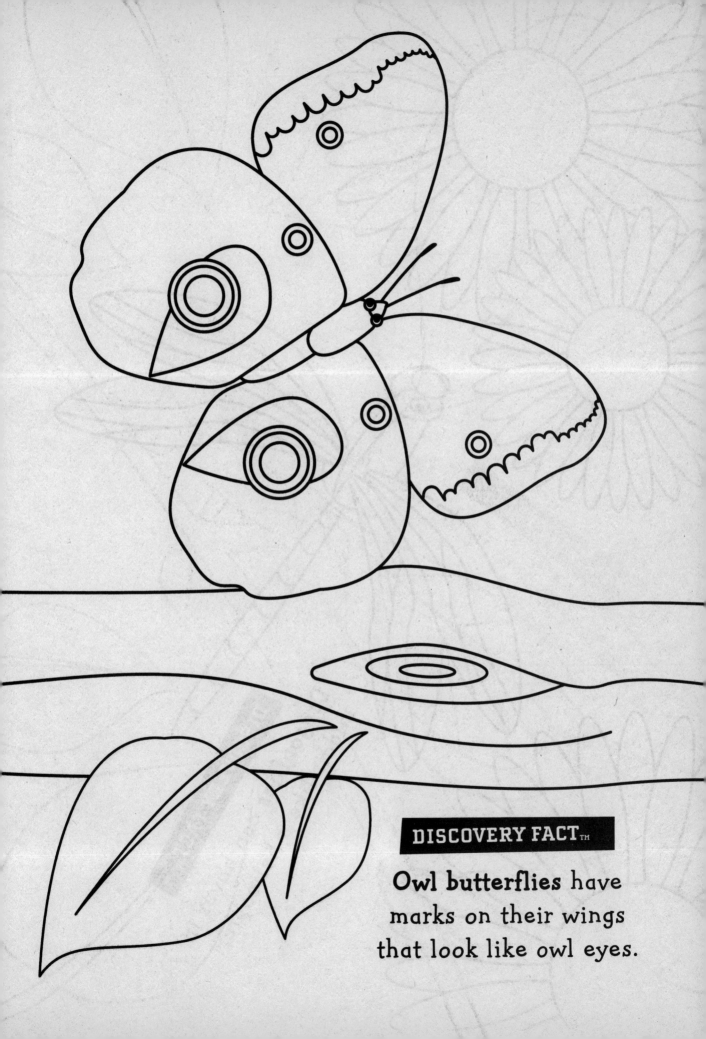

DISCOVERY FACT™

Owl butterflies have
marks on their wings
that look like owl eyes.

DISCOVERY FACT™

Dragonflies can hover in midair like a helicopter!

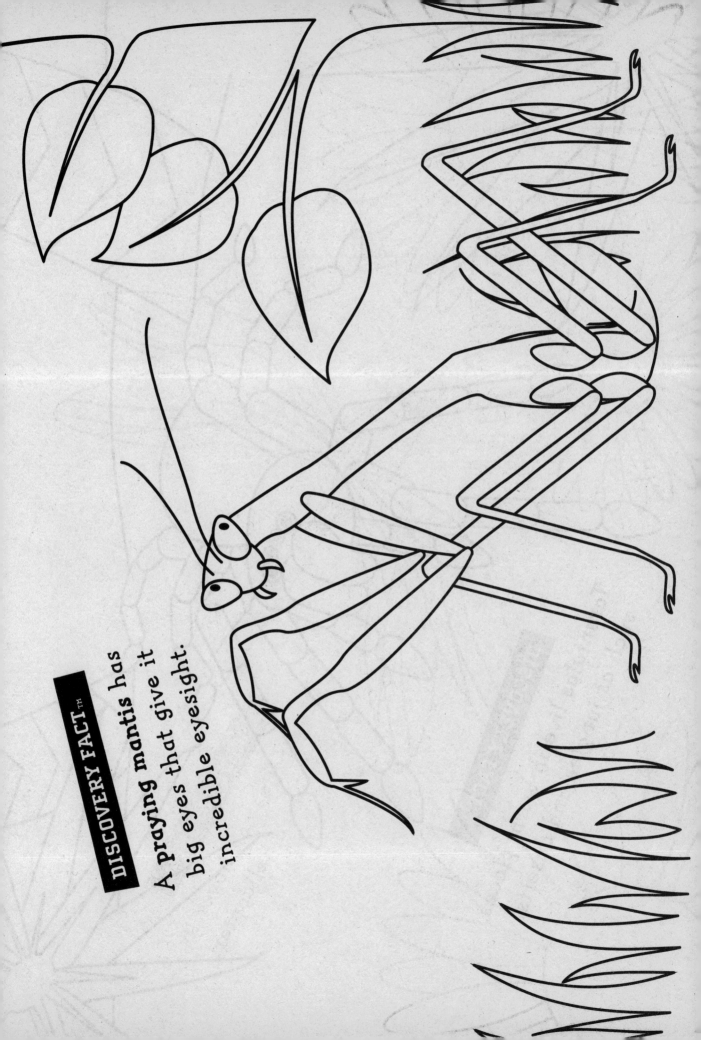

DISCOVERY FACT™

A praying mantis has big eyes that give it incredible eyesight.

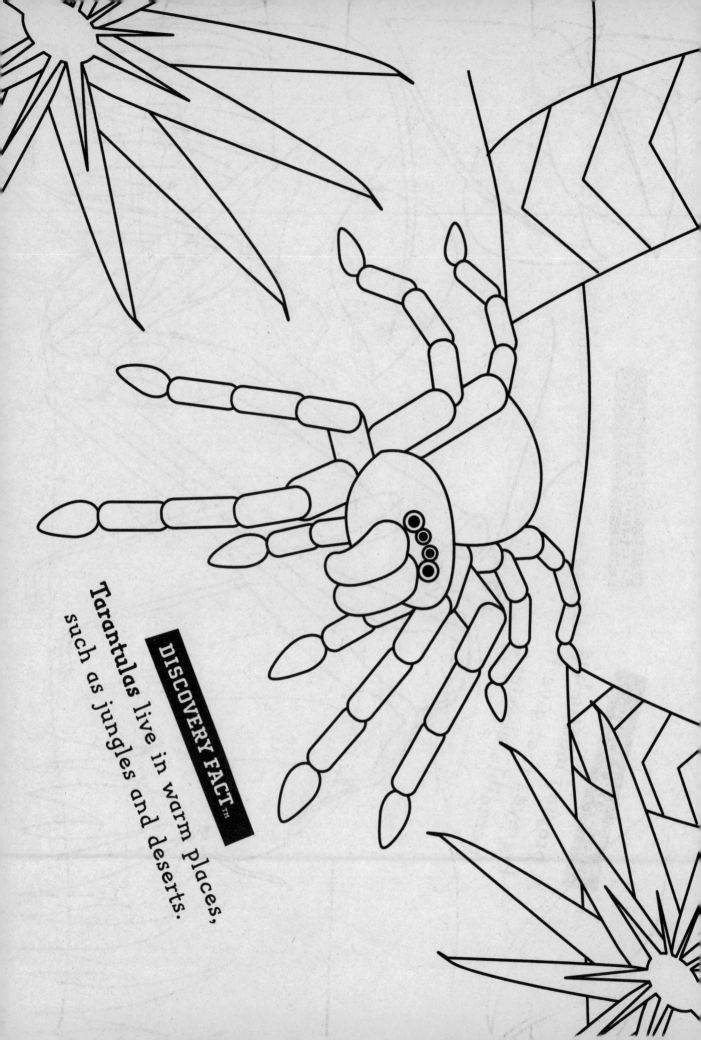

DISCOVERY FACT™

Tarantulas live in warm places, such as jungles and deserts.

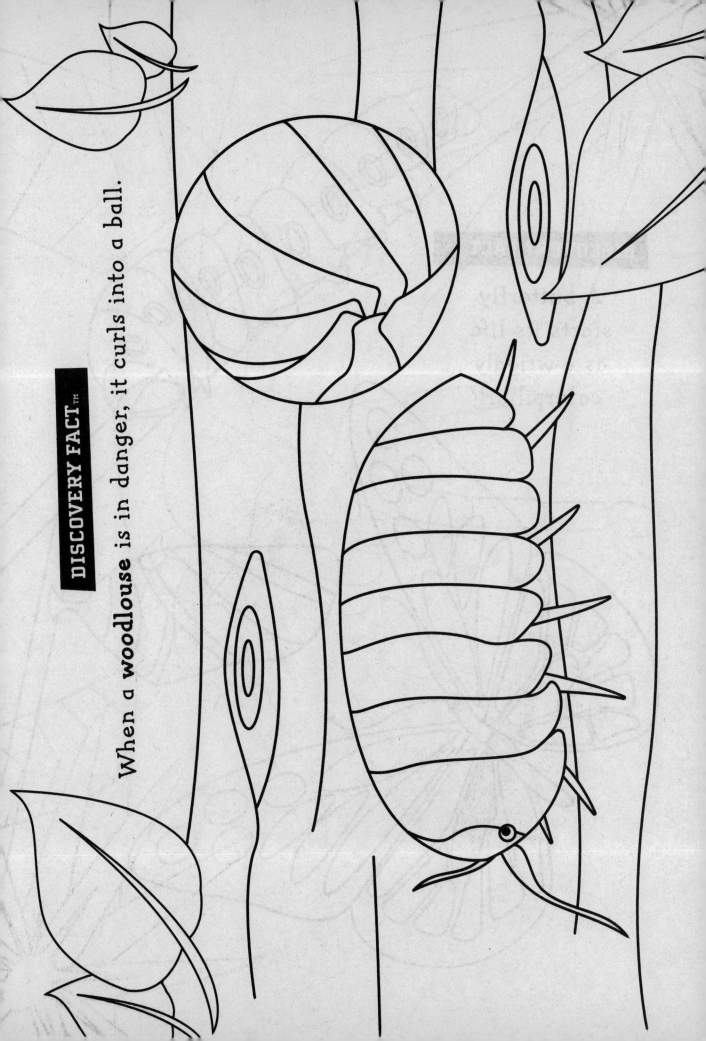

When a **woodlouse** is in danger, it curls into a ball.

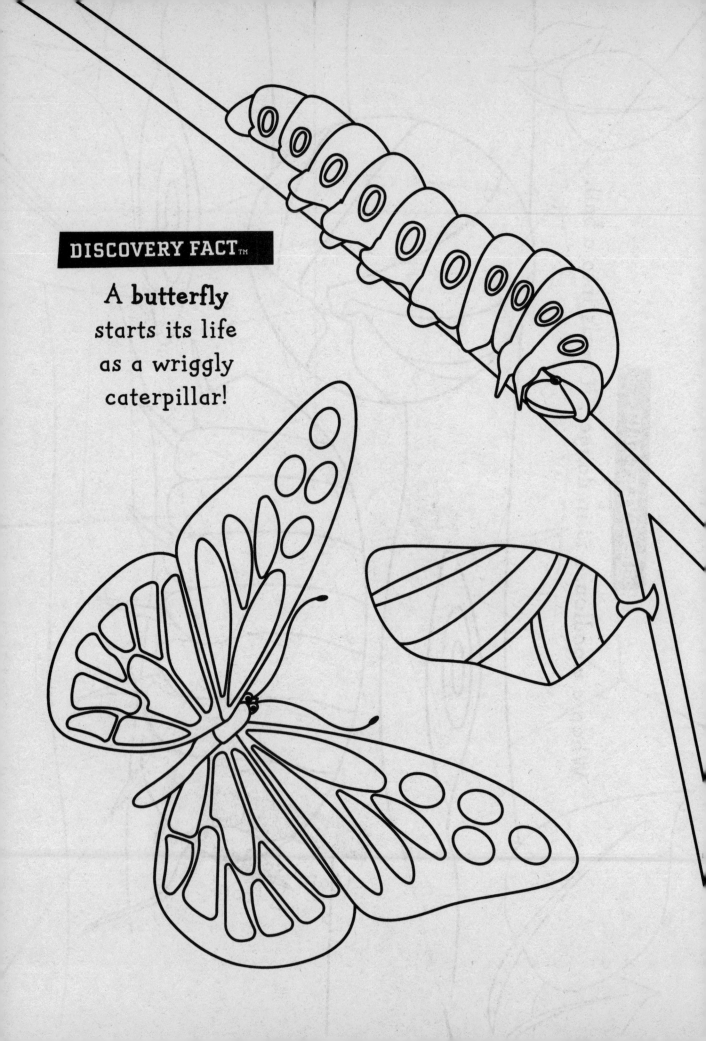

DISCOVERY FACT ™

A **butterfly** starts its life as a wriggly caterpillar!

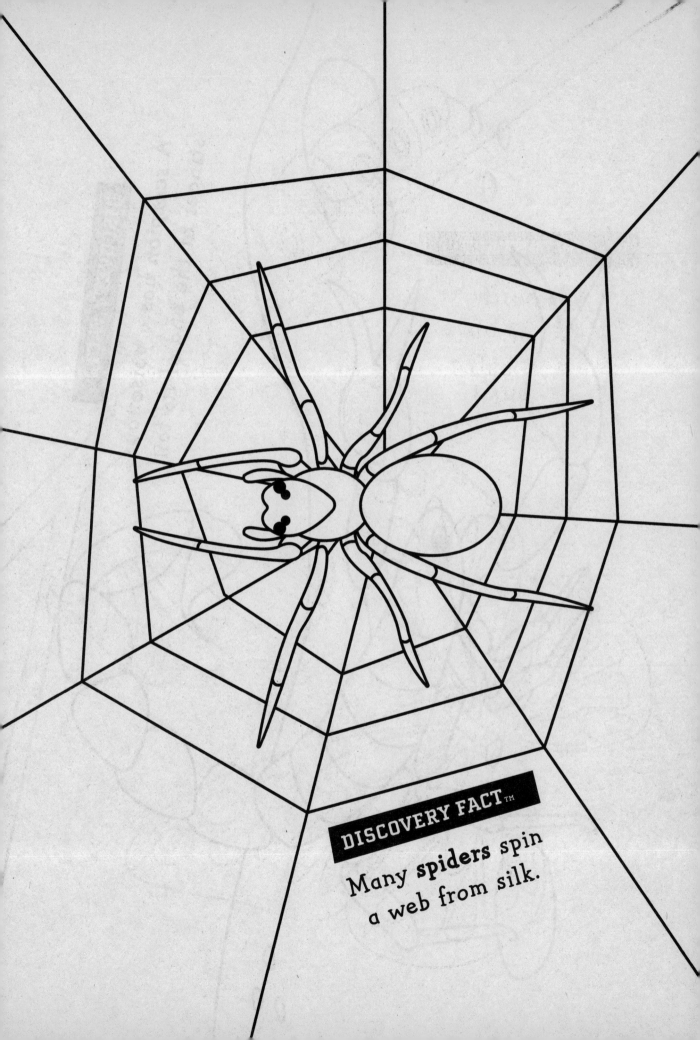

DISCOVERY FACT™

Many **spiders** spin a web from silk.

A scorpion has a poisonous stinger at the end of its tail!

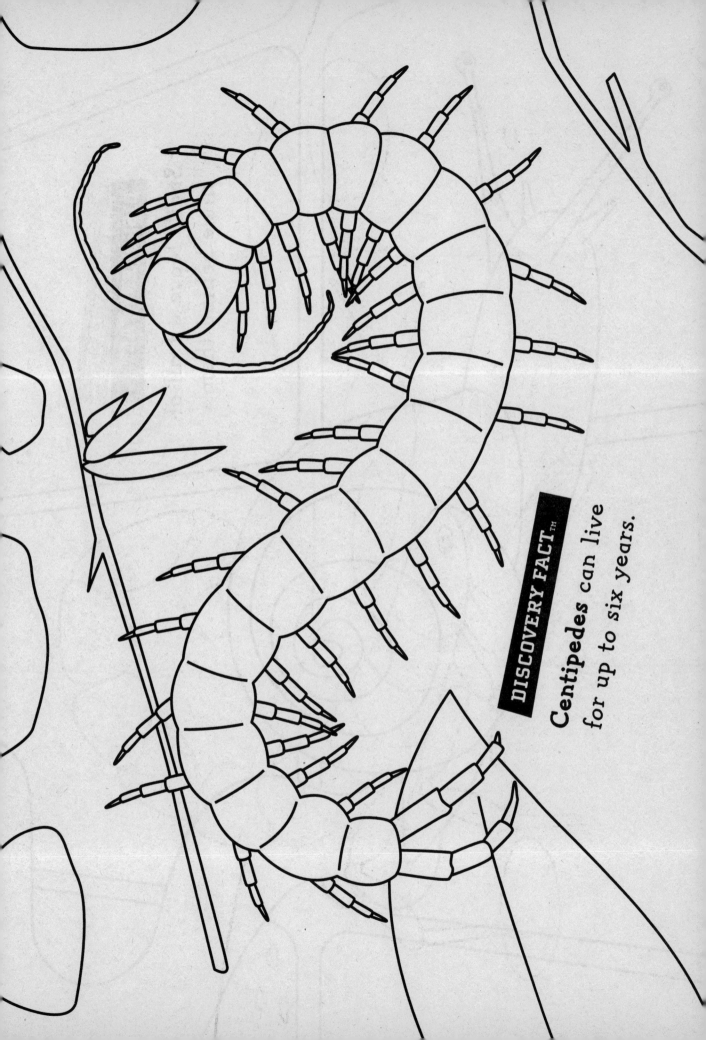

Centipedes can live for up to six years.

Snails leave a trail of slime behind them.

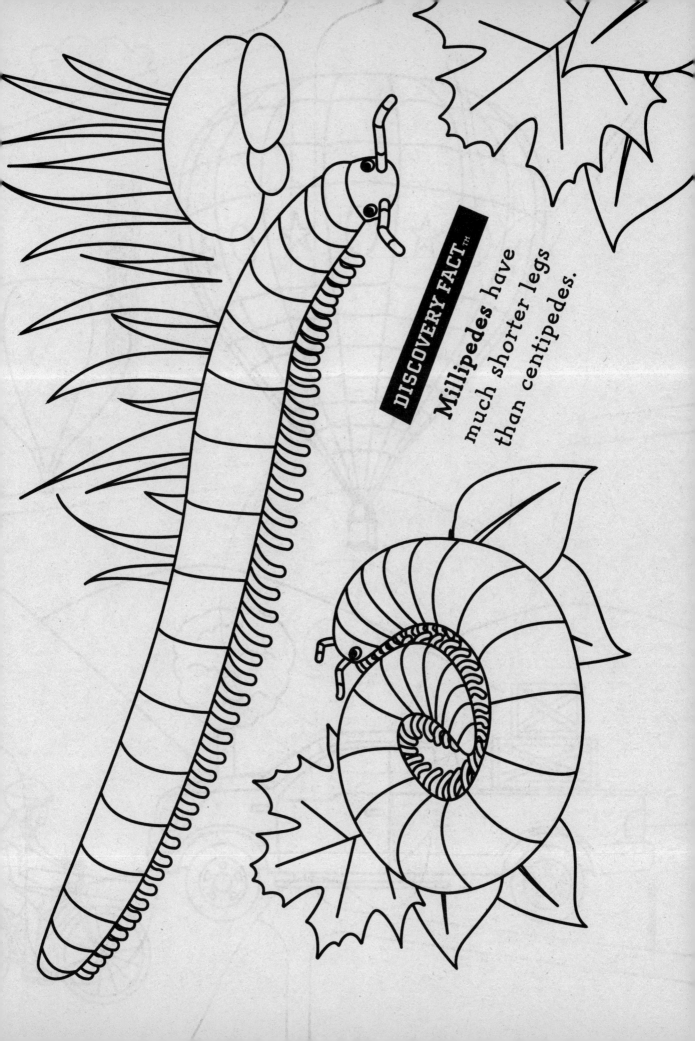

DISCOVERY FACT™

Millipedes have much shorter legs than centipedes.

VEHICLES

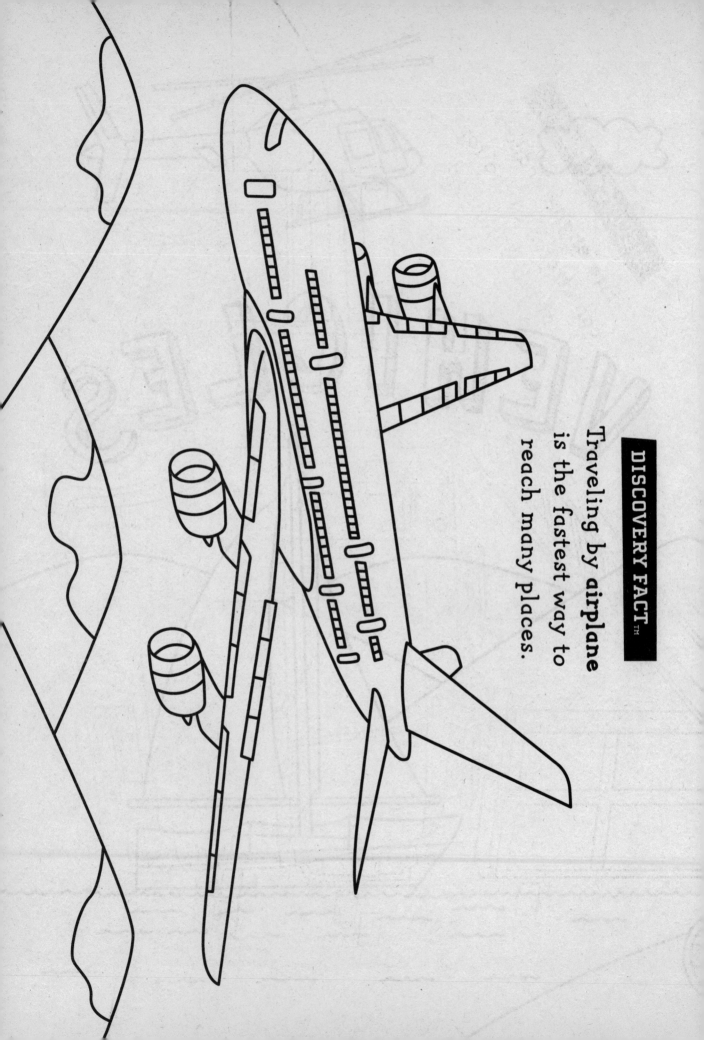

Traveling by airplane is the fastest way to reach many places.

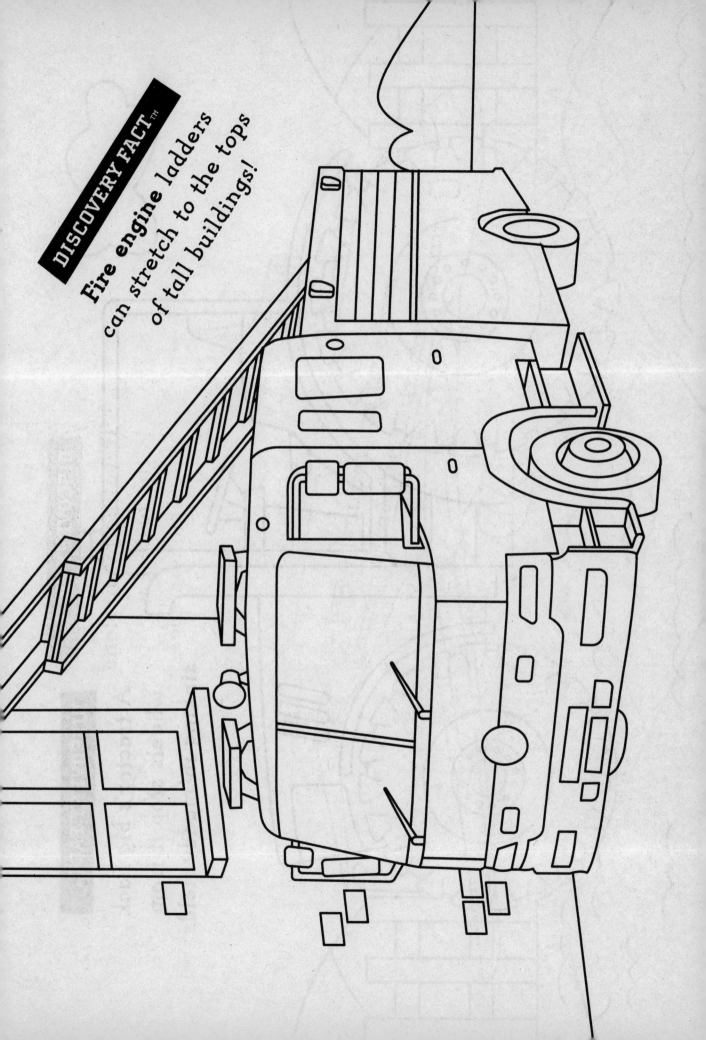

DISCOVERY FACT™

Fire engine ladders can stretch to the tops of tall buildings!

DISCOVERY FACT™

A tractor's big back wheels stop it from sinking in muddy fields.

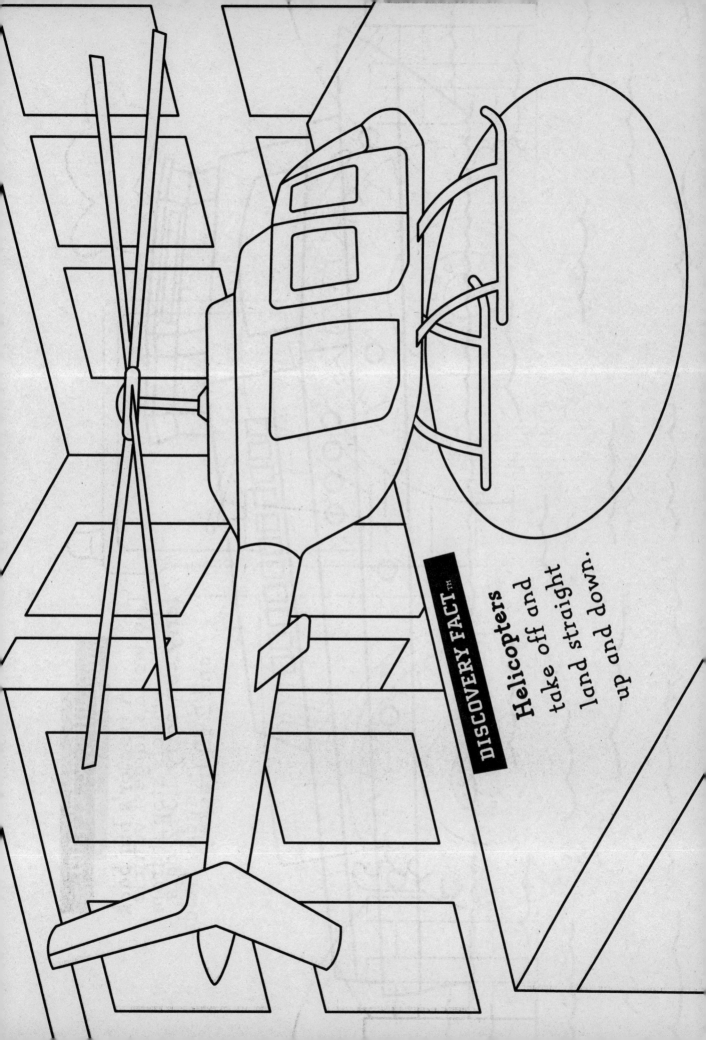

DISCOVERY FACT™

Helicopters
take off and
land straight
up and down.

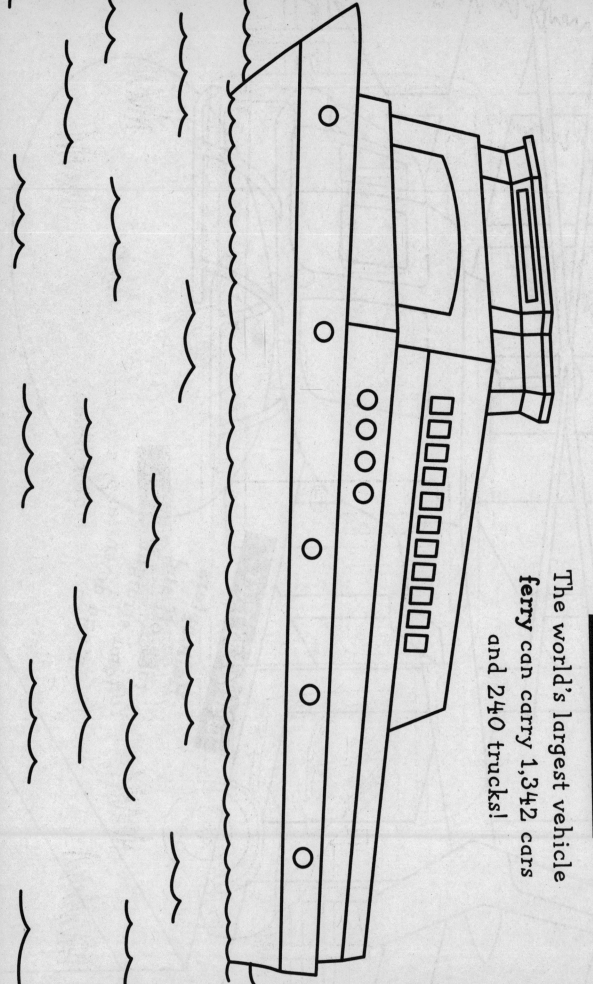

The world's largest vehicle ferry can carry 1,342 cars and 240 trucks!

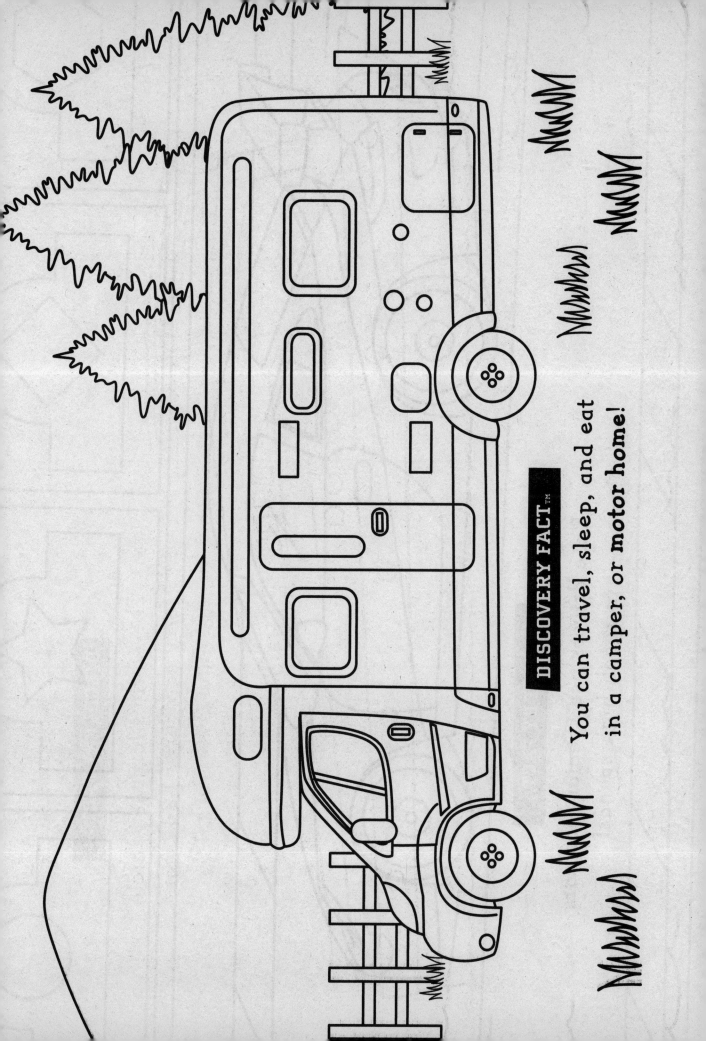

DISCOVERY FACT™

You can travel, sleep, and eat in a camper, or motor home!

DISCOVERY FACT™

Race drivers use special race cars
to reach high speeds!

DISCOVERY FACT™

Motorcyclists wear helmets and protective clothing.

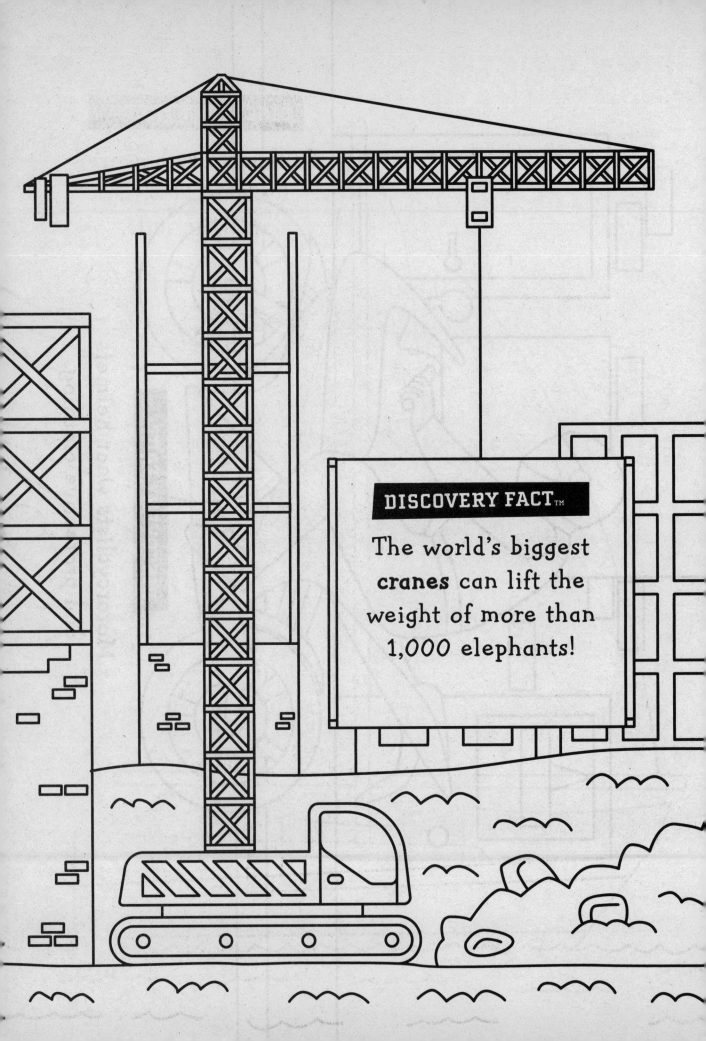

DISCOVERY FACT™

The world's biggest **cranes** can lift the weight of more than 1,000 elephants!

Sailboats are powered by wind blowing on their sails.

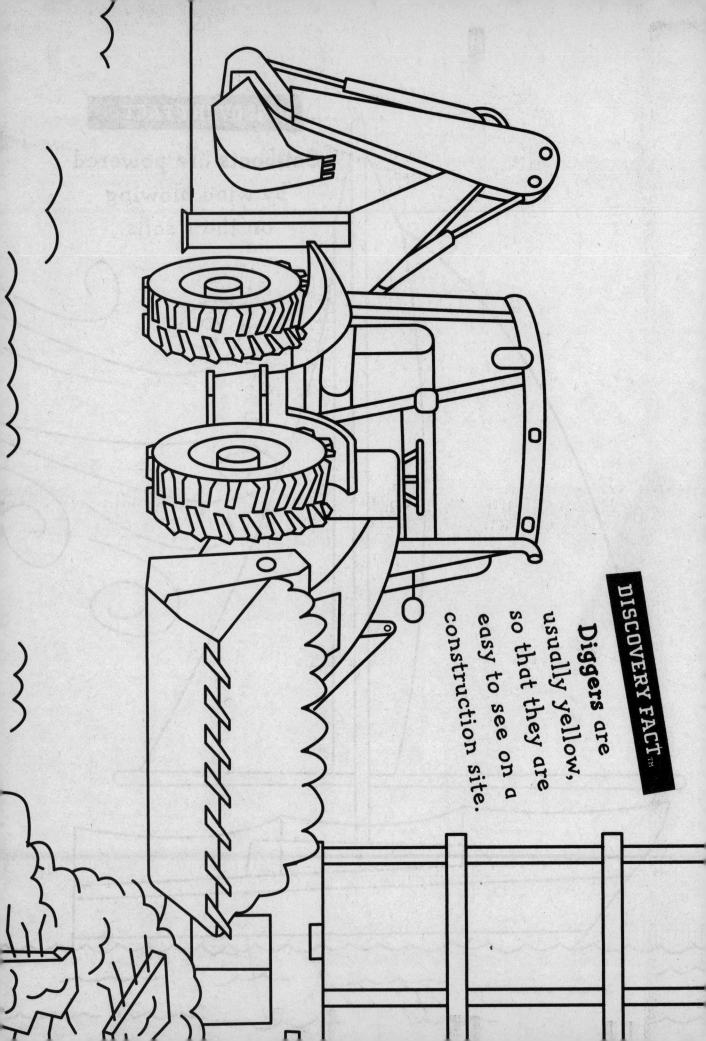

Diggers are usually yellow, so that they are easy to see on a construction site.

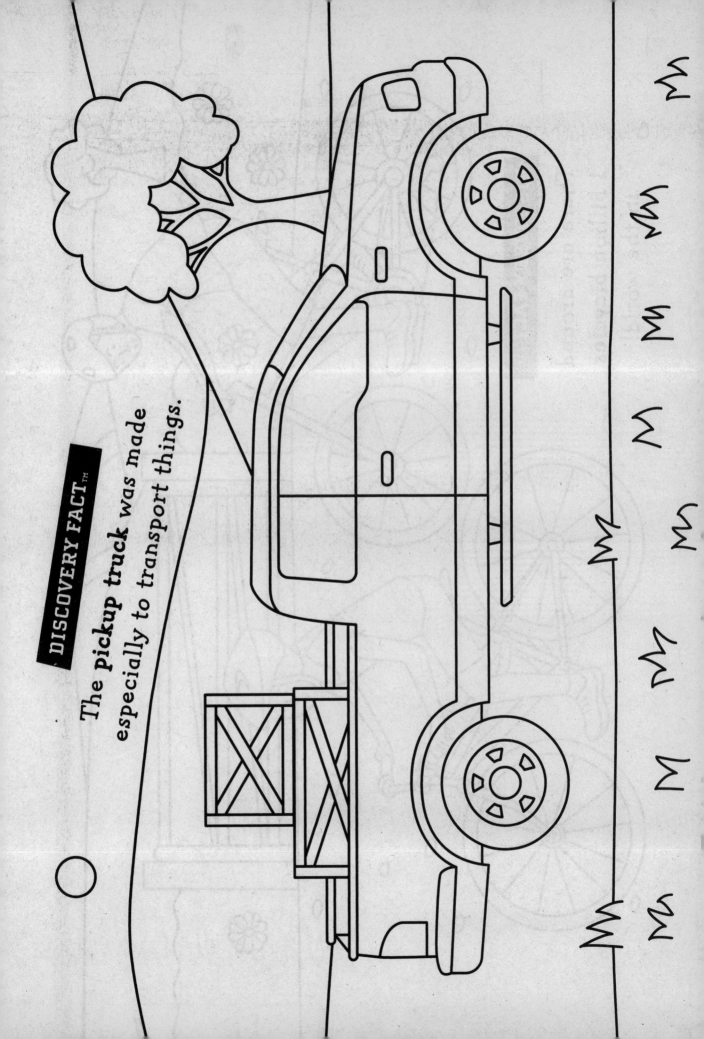

DISCOVERY FACT™

The pickup truck was made especially to transport things.

DISCOVERY FACT™

There are around
1 billion **bicycles**
in the world!

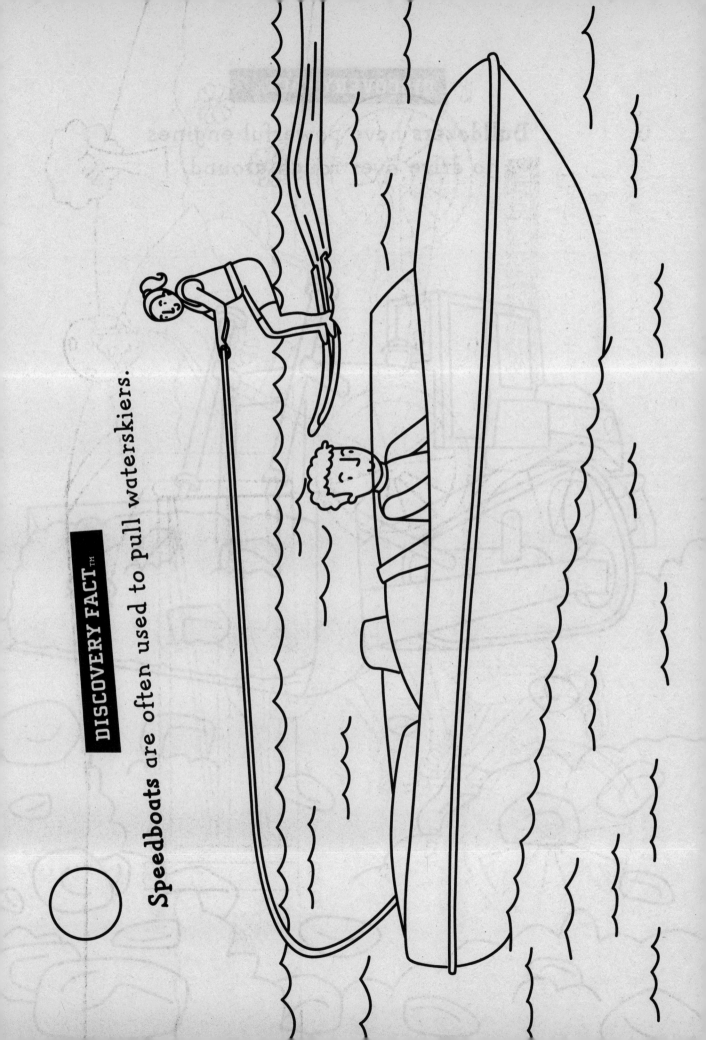

Speedboats are often used to pull waterskiers.

Bulldozers have powerful engines
to drive over rough ground.

The first human flight was
by **hot air balloon**.

DISCOVERY FACT™

A stretch limousine can hold up to 20 people!

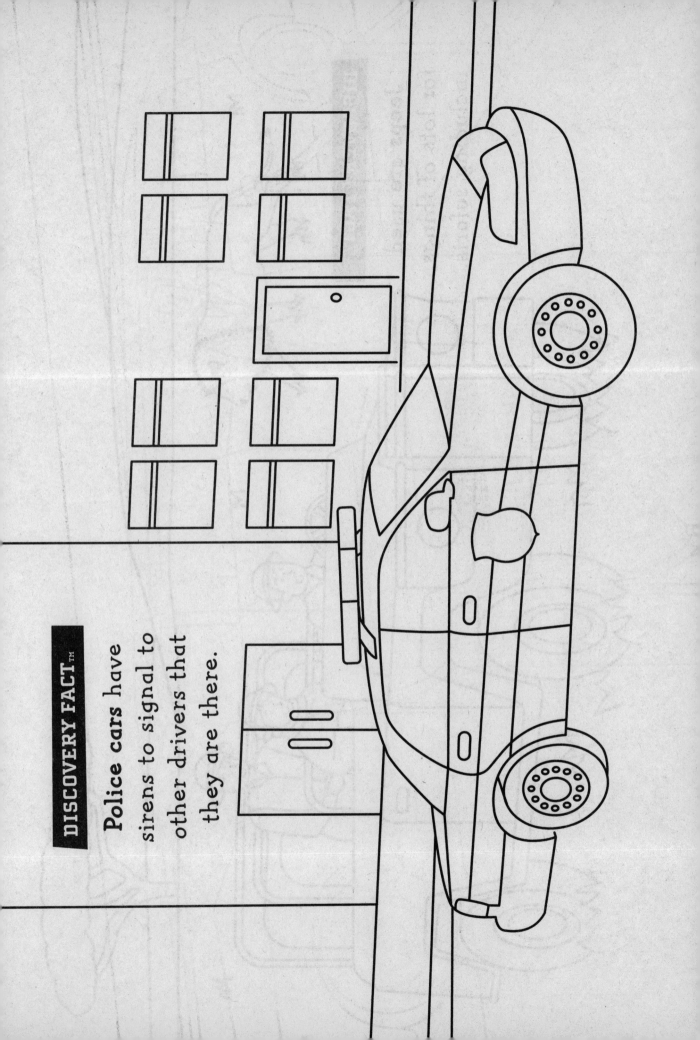

DISCOVERY FACT™

Police cars have sirens to signal to other drivers that they are there.

DISCOVERY FACT™

Jeeps are used for lots of things, including safaris.

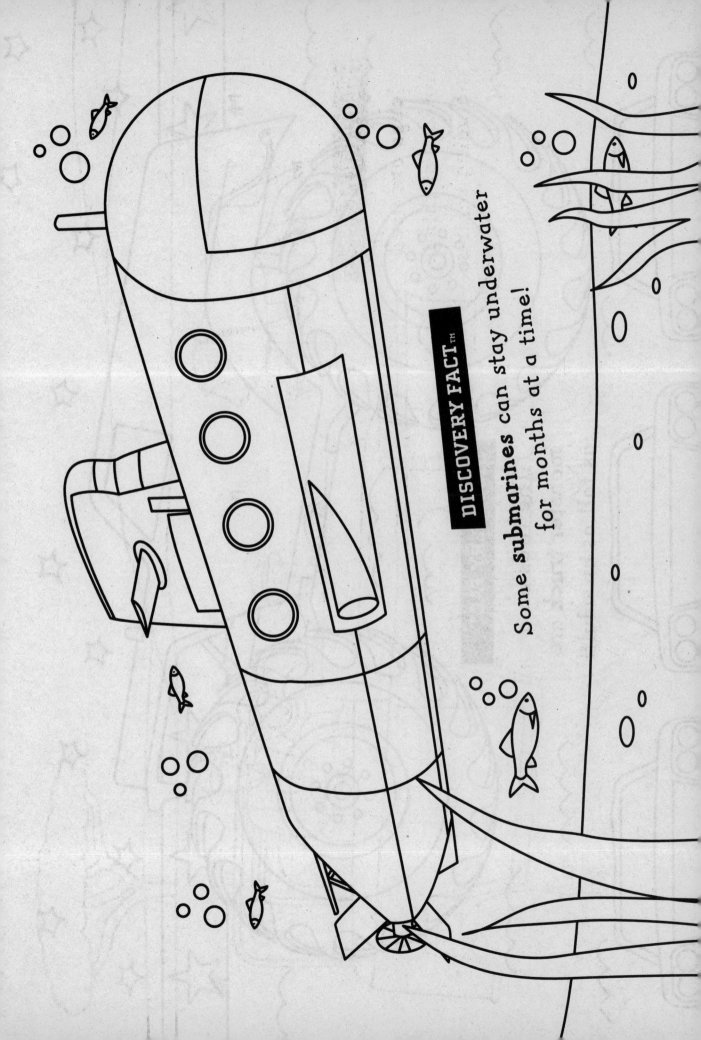

DISCOVERY FACT™

Some submarines can stay underwater for months at a time!

DISCOVERY FACT™

The tires on a monster truck are as tall as an adult!

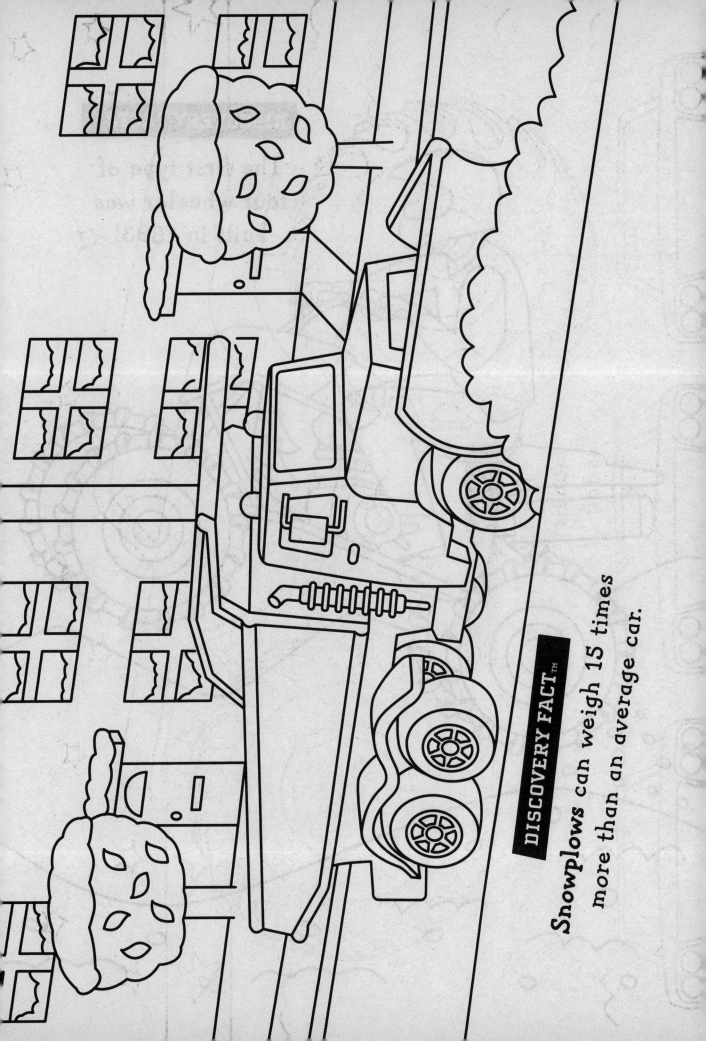

DISCOVERY FACT™

Snowplows can weigh 15 times more than an average car.

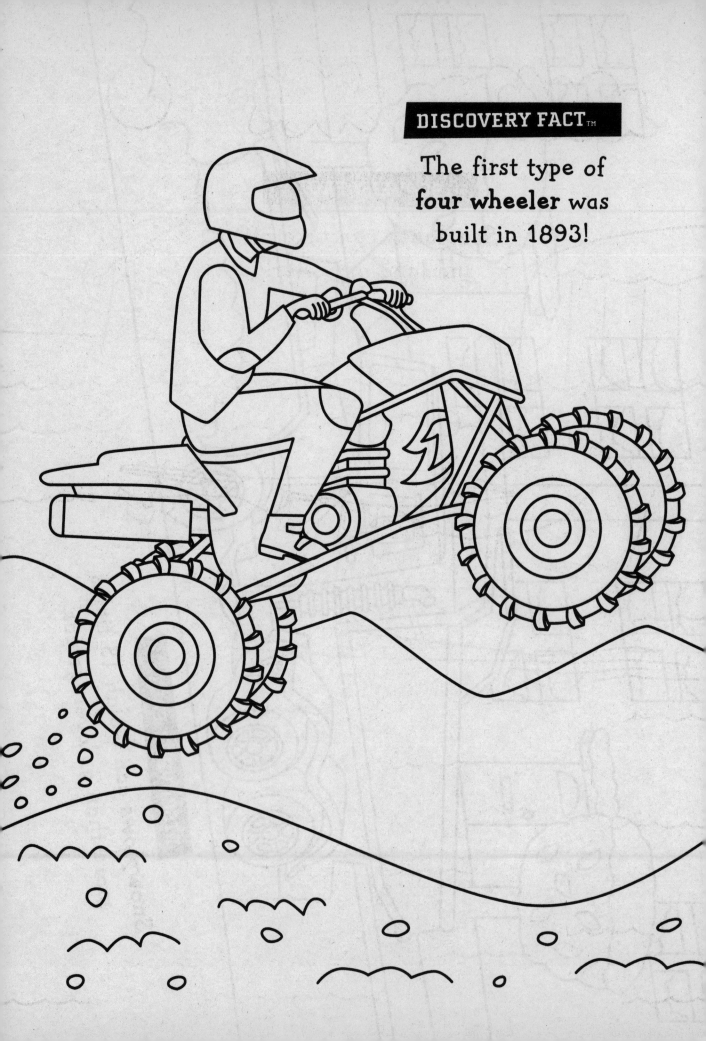

DISCOVERY FACT™

The first type of **four wheeler** was built in 1893!

DISCOVERY FACT™

Seaplanes can take off
and land on water!

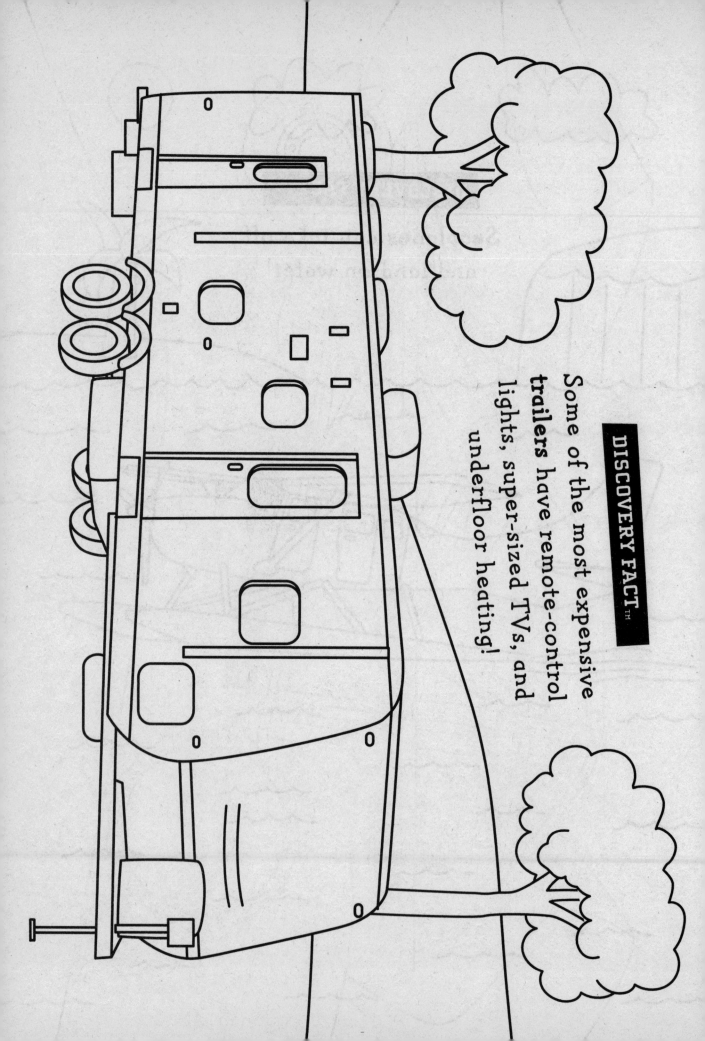

Some of the most expensive trailers have remote-control lights, super-sized TVs, and underfloor heating!

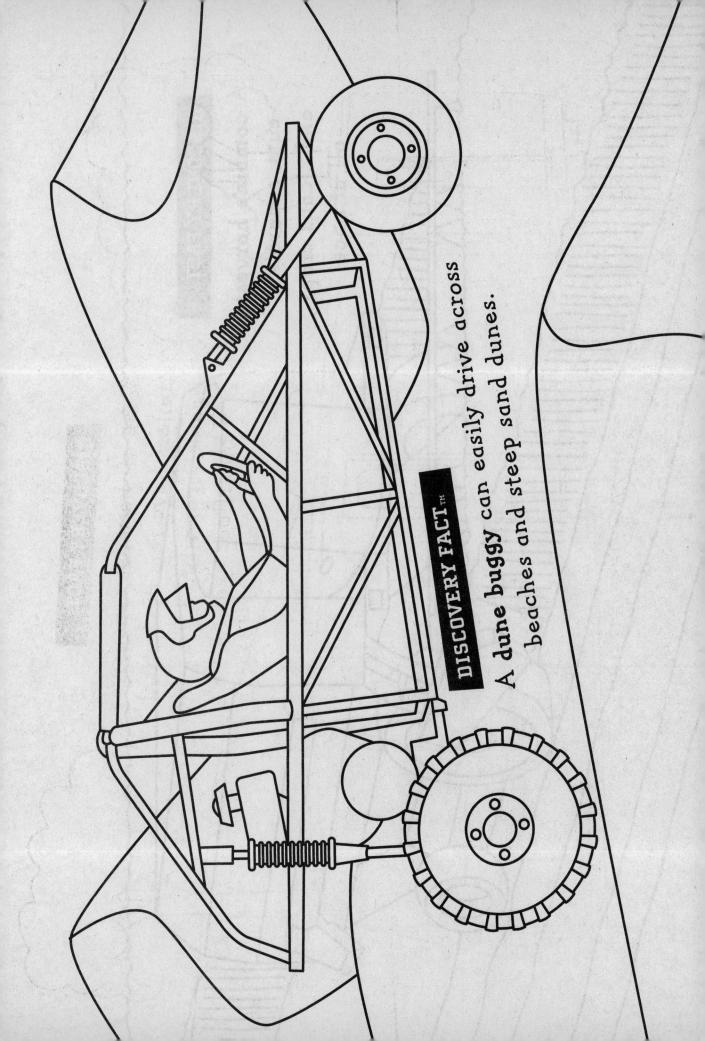

DISCOVERY FACT™

A dune buggy can easily drive across beaches and steep sand dunes.

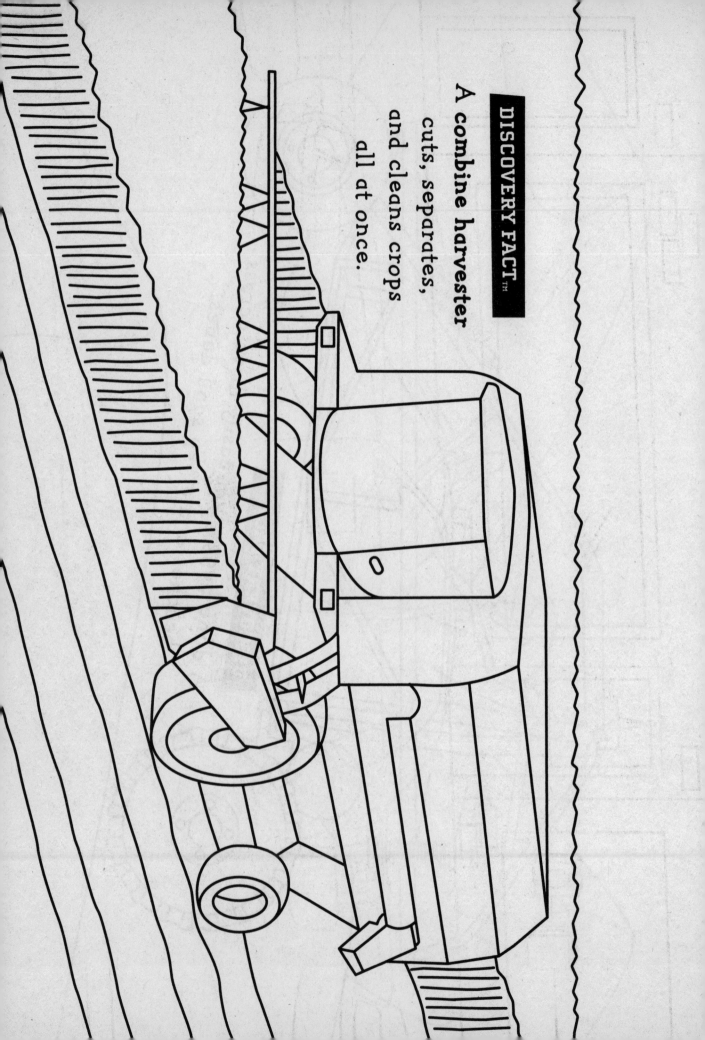

DISCOVERY FACT™

A combine harvester
cuts, separates,
and cleans crops
all at once.

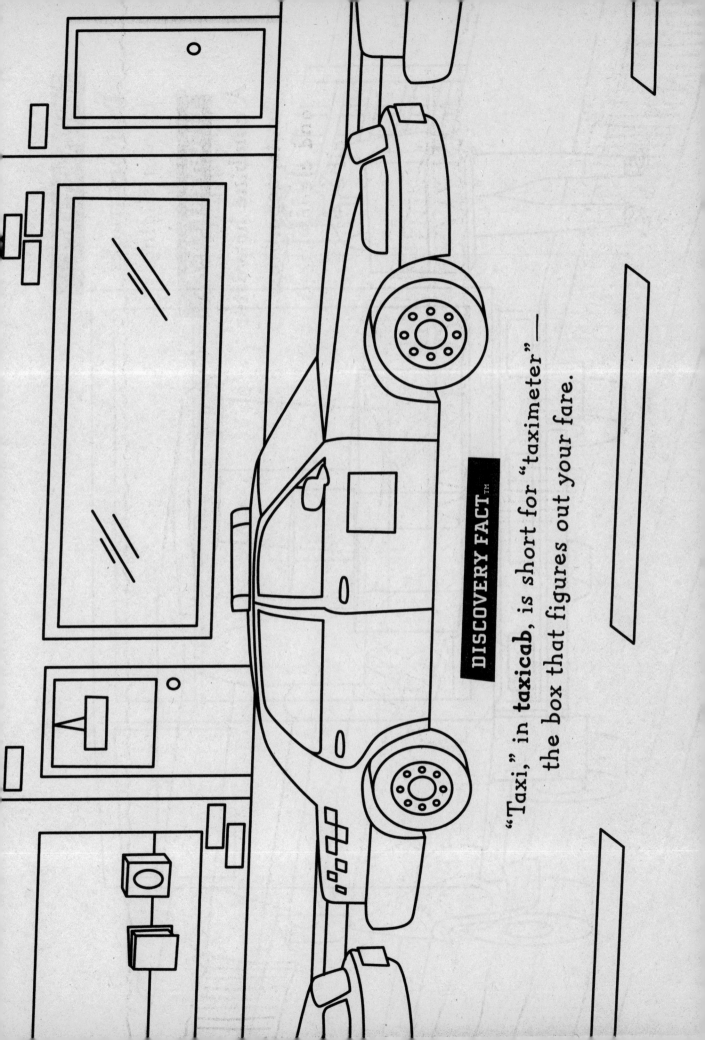

DISCOVERY FACT™

"Taxi," in taxicab, is short for "taximeter"— the box that figures out your fare.

DISCOVERY FACT™

Delivery trucks have a sliding door at the back for loading.

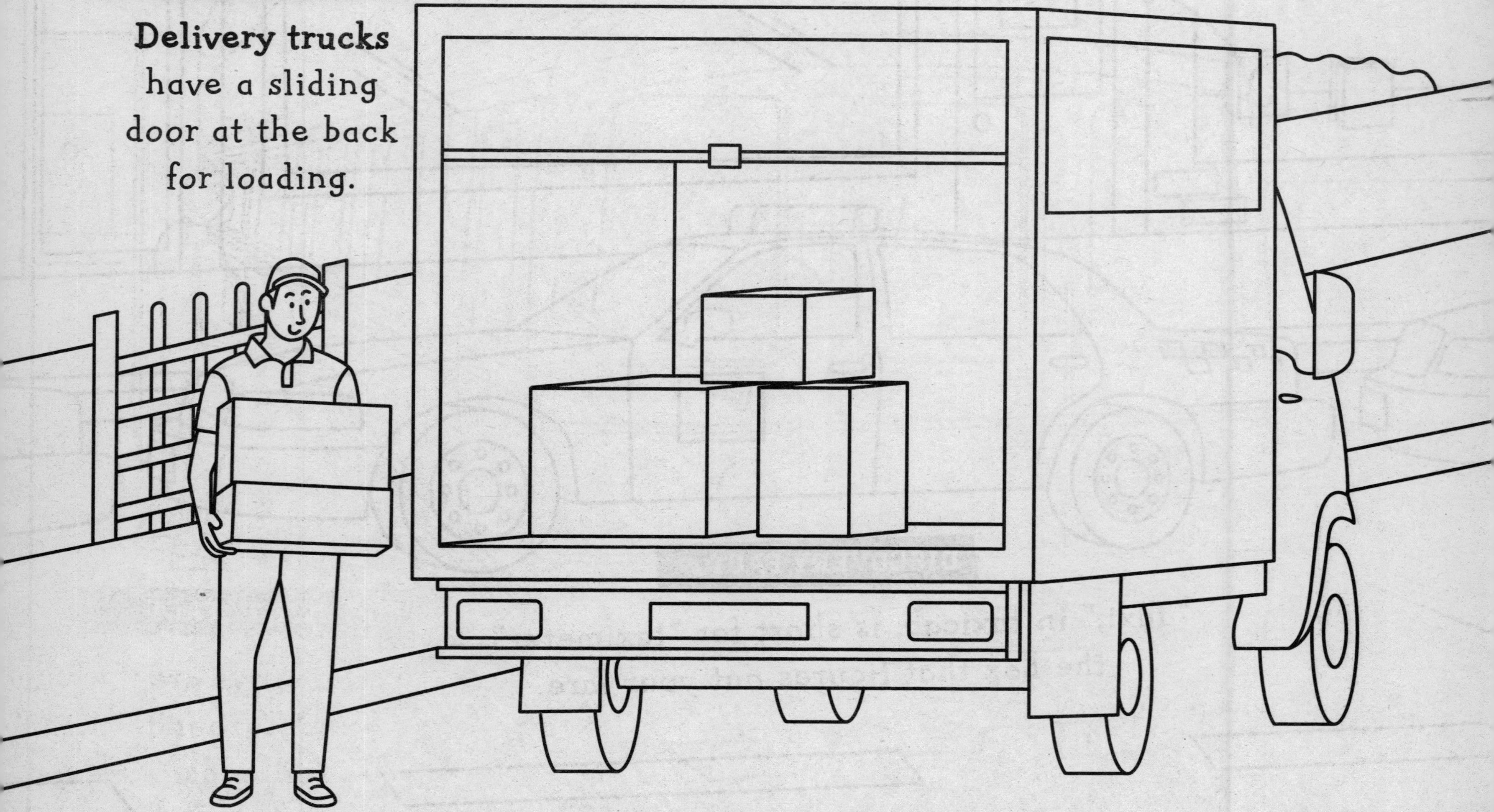

DISCOVERY FACT™

Subways are underground railroads.

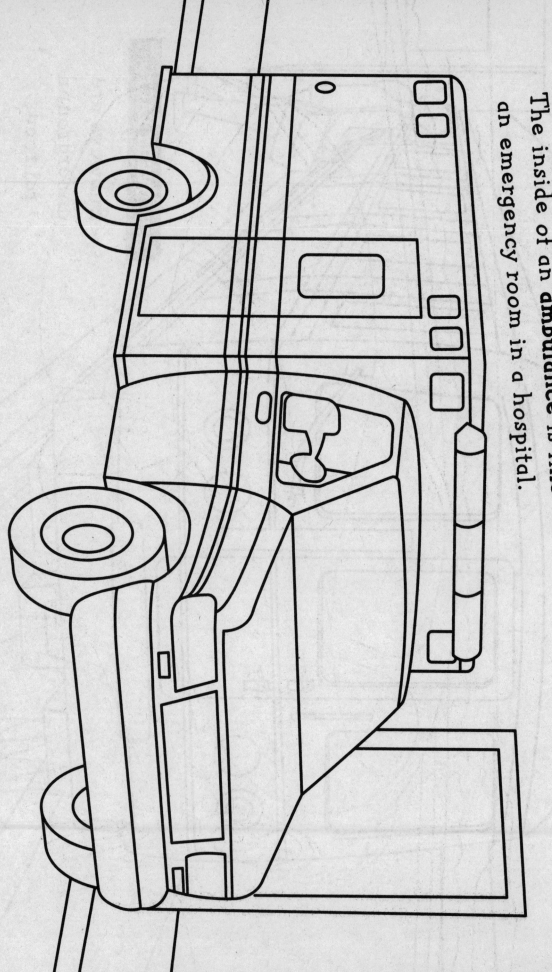

The inside of an ambulance is like an emergency room in a hospital.

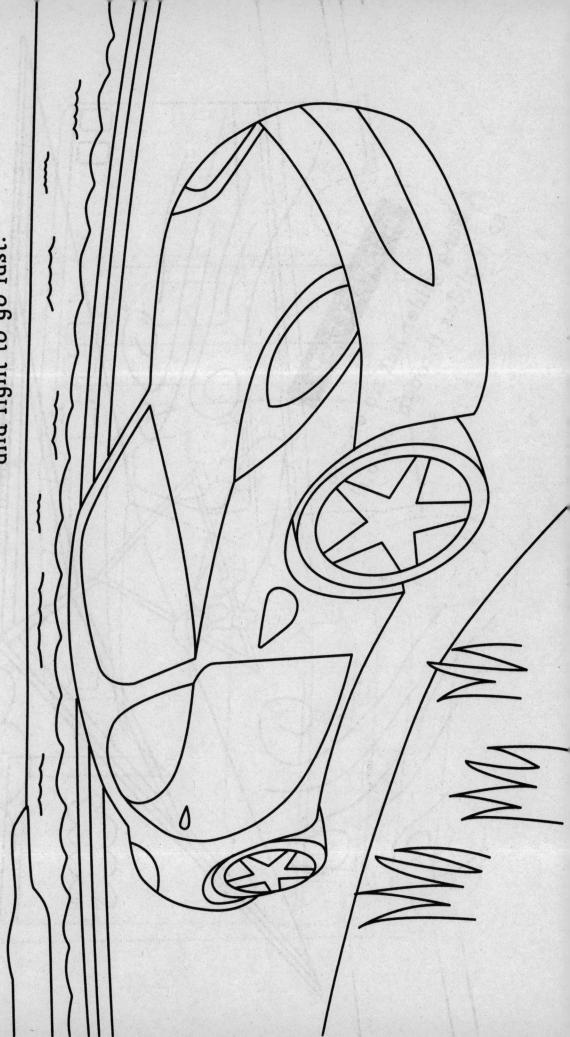

Sports cars need to be small and light to go fast.

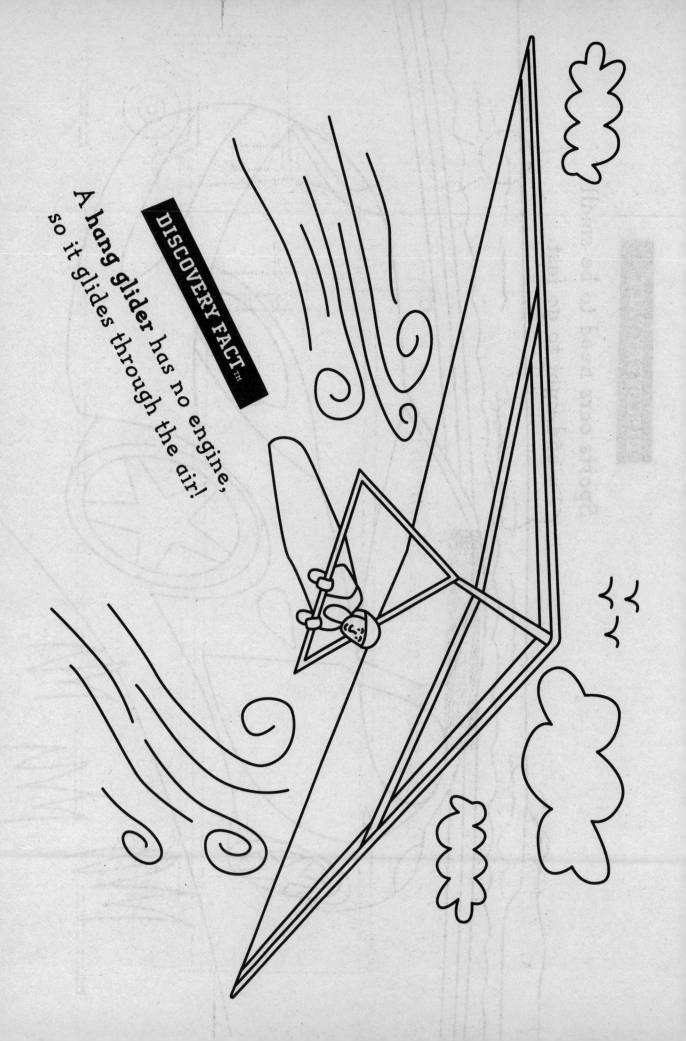

DISCOVERY FACT™

A **hang glider** has no engine, so it glides through the air!

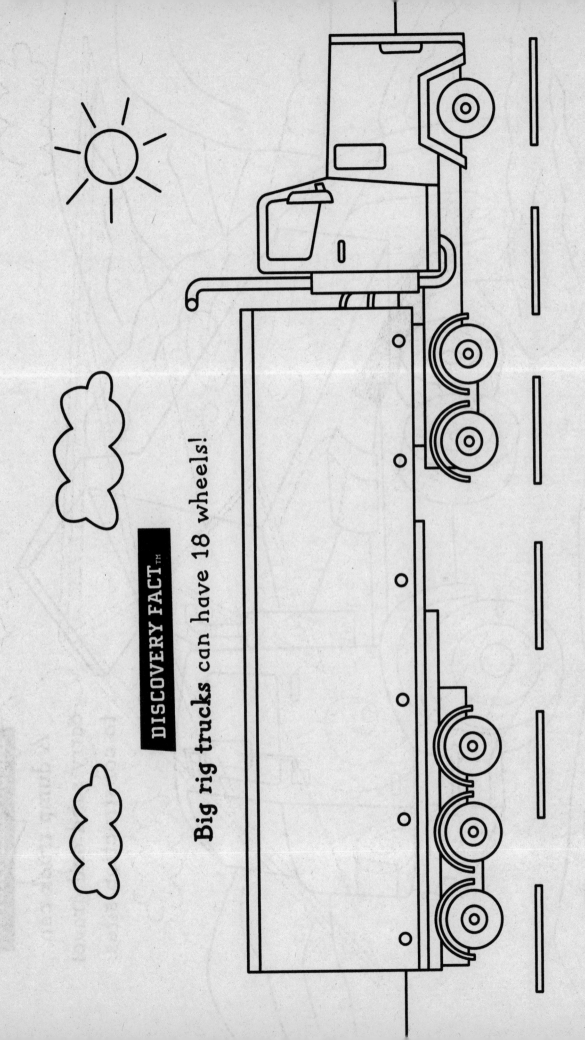

DISCOVERY FACT™

Big rig trucks can have 18 wheels!

DISCOVERY FACT™

A **dump truck** can carry sand and gravel to construction sites.

DISCOVERY FACT™

Hovercrafts can hover
over land and water!

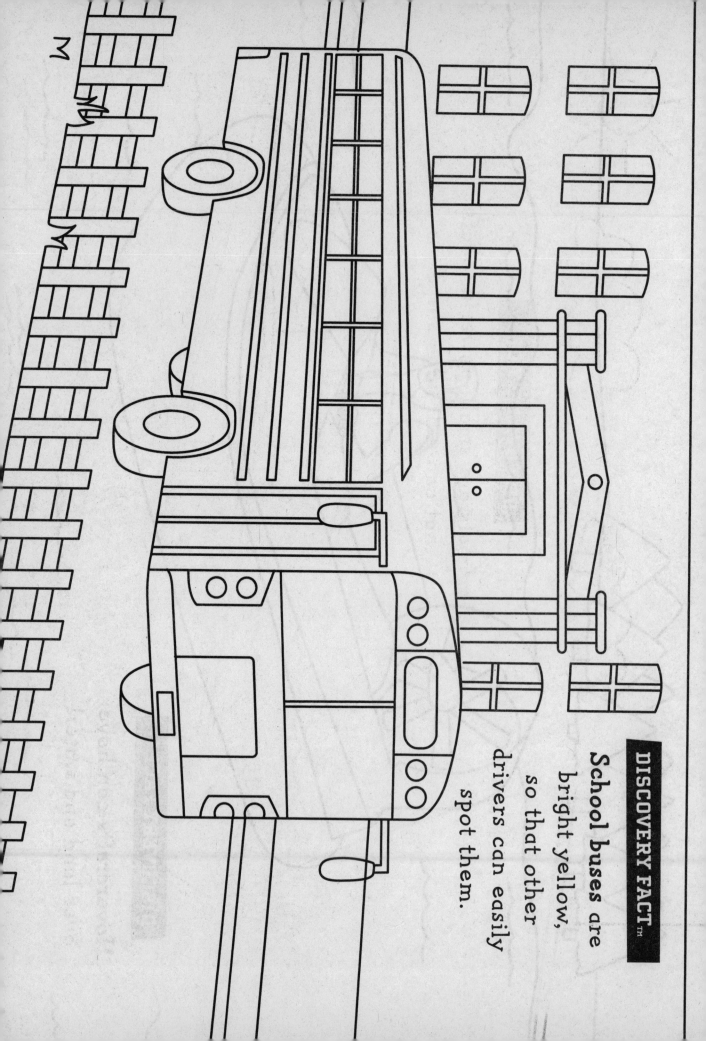

DISCOVERY FACT™

School buses are bright yellow, so that other drivers can easily spot them.

DISCOVERY FACT™

Tugboats are small, powerful boats that can pull huge ships!

DISCOVERY FACT™

Stunt bikes can be used for stunts, such as wheelies and backward riding!

Trains are powered by steam, diesel, or electricity.

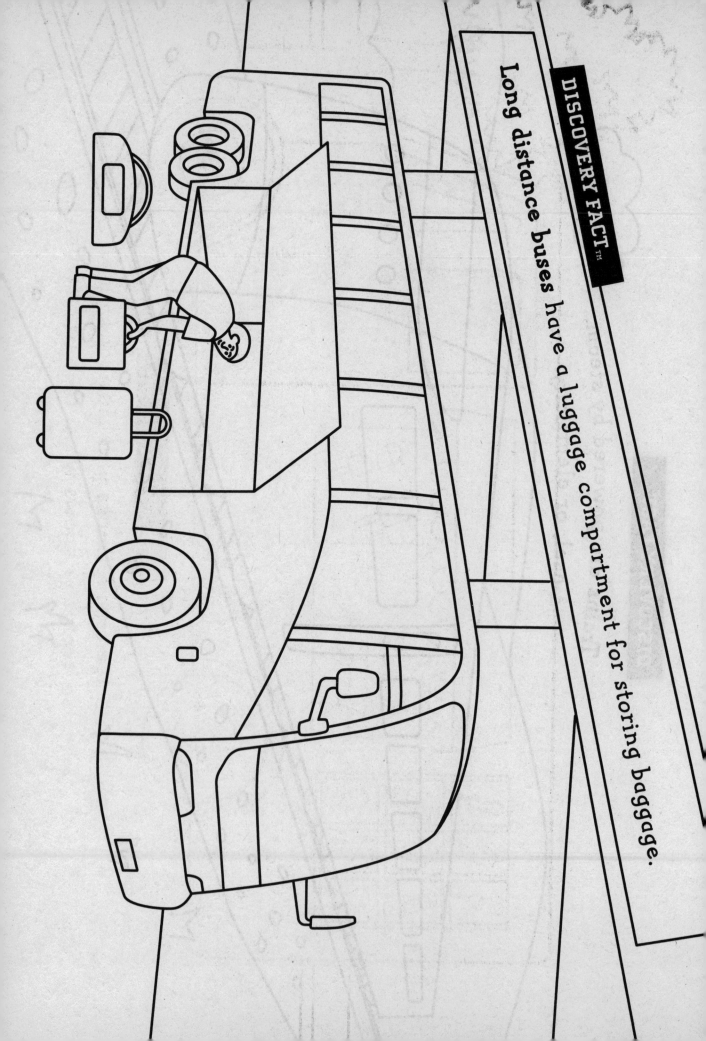

Long distance buses have a luggage compartment for storing baggage.

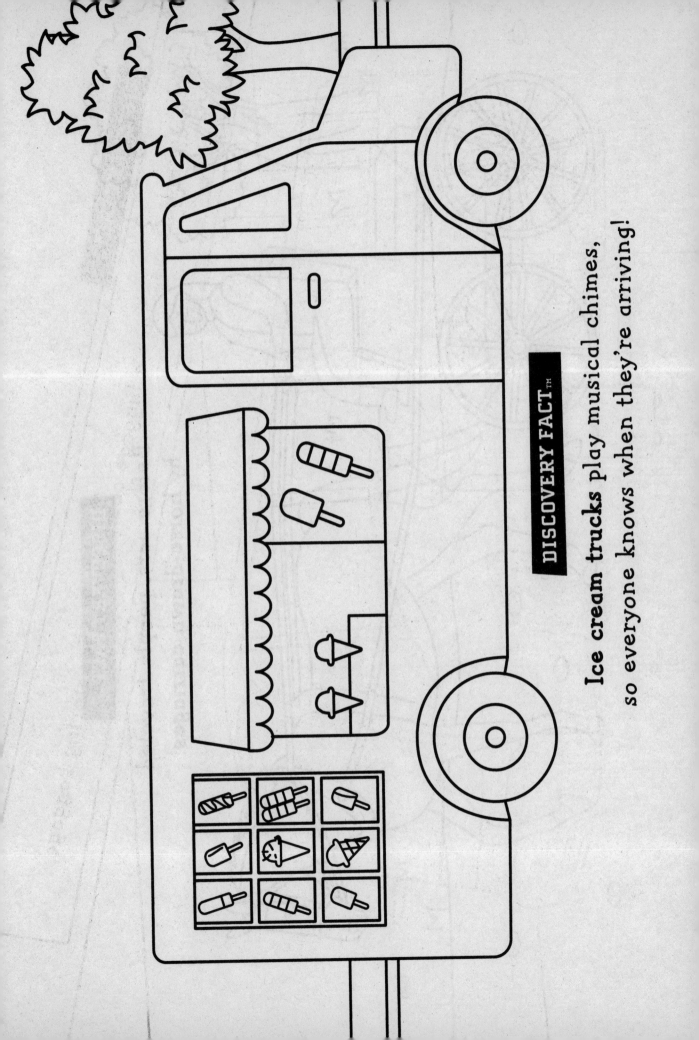

Ice cream trucks play musical chimes, so everyone knows when they're arriving!

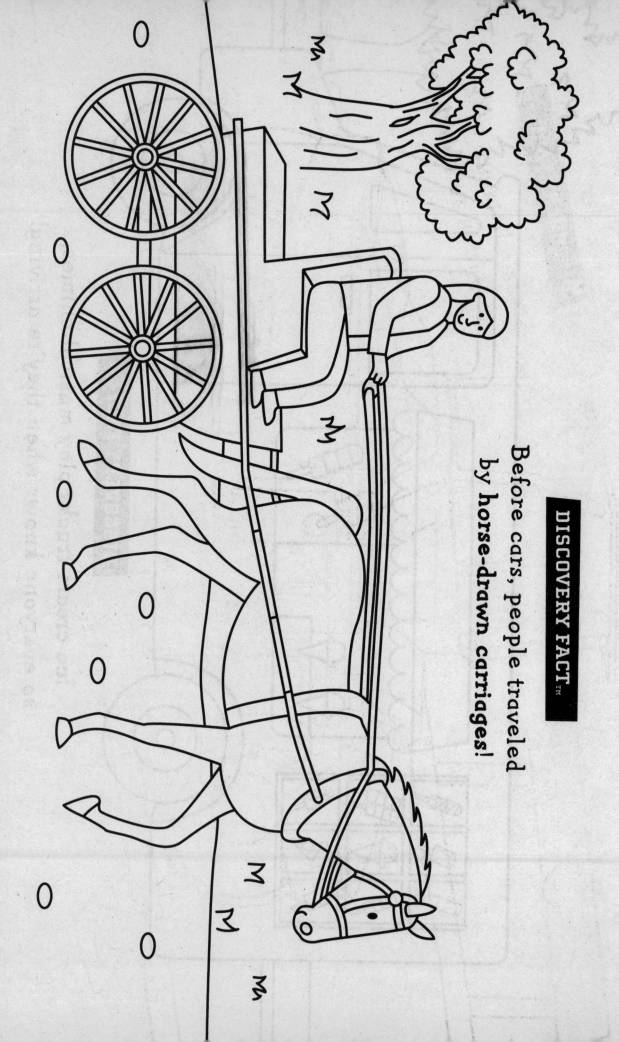

DISCOVERY FACT™

Before cars, people traveled by horse-drawn carriages!

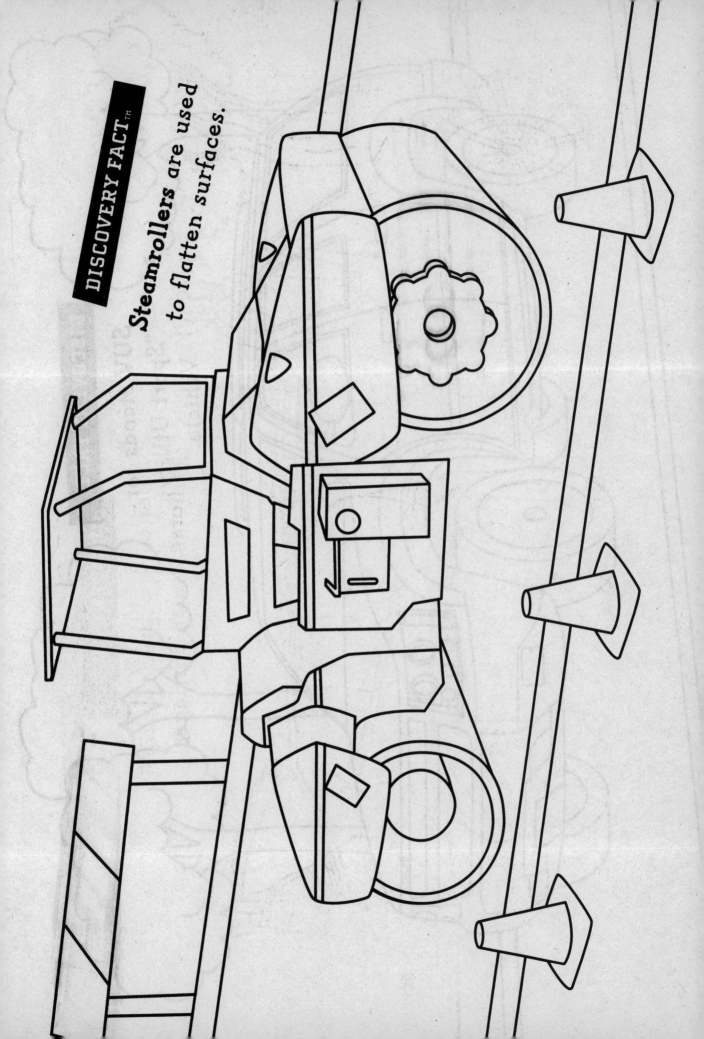

DISCOVERY FACT™

Steamrollers are used to flatten surfaces.

DISCOVERY FACT™

SUV stands for "Sport Utility Vehicle."

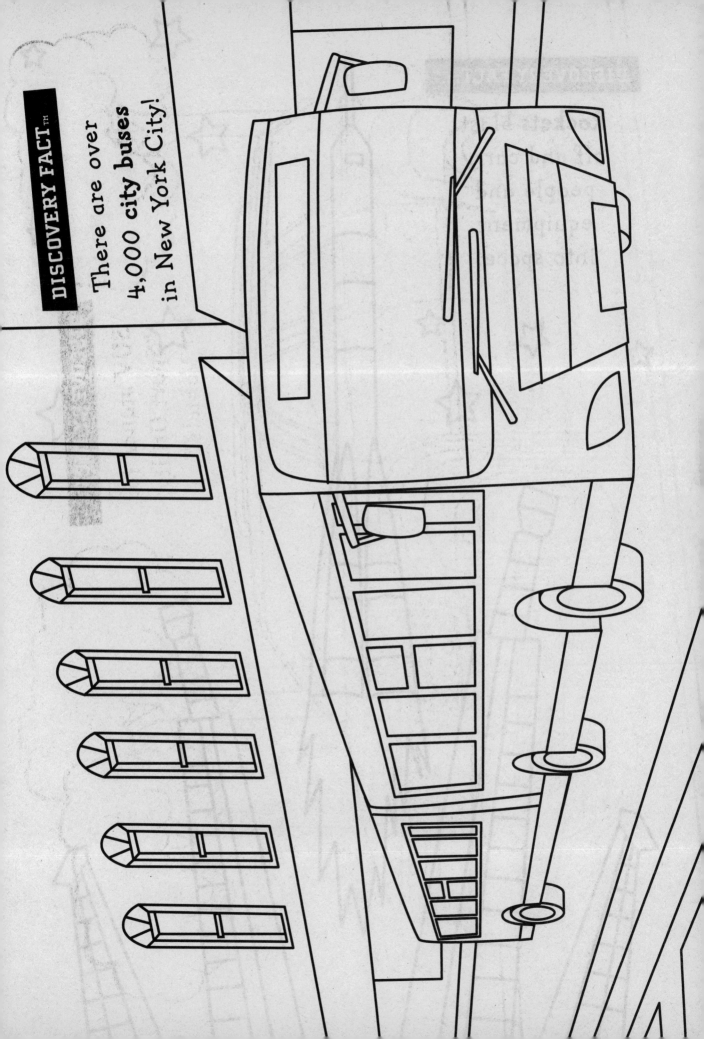

DISCOVERY FACT™

There are over 4,000 city buses in New York City!

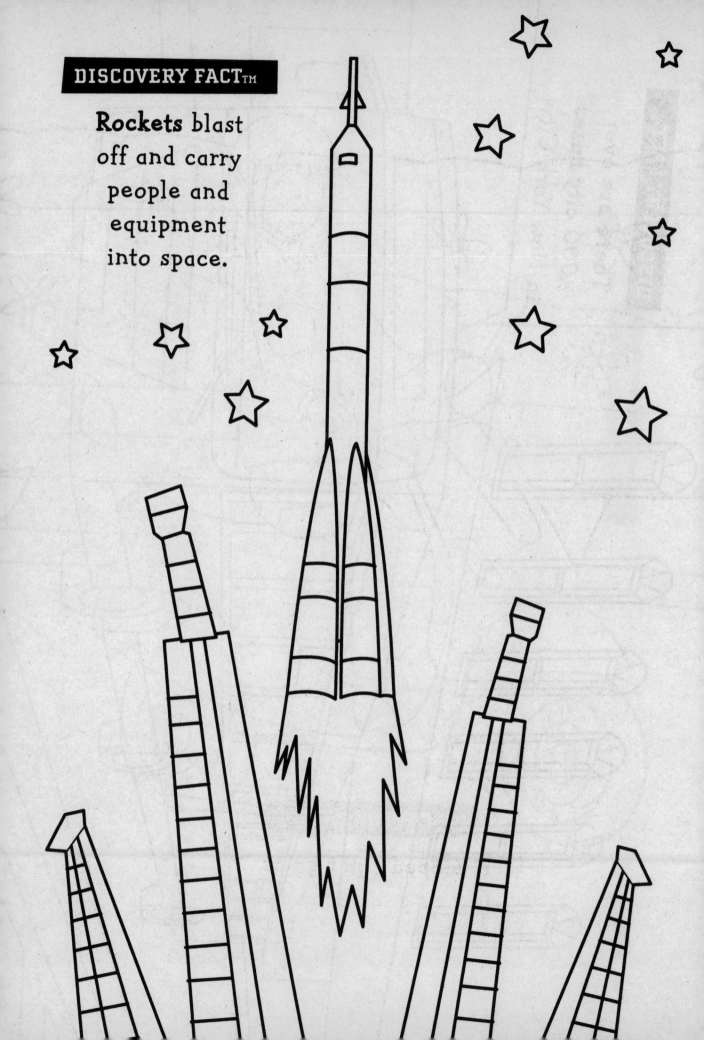

DISCOVERY FACT™

Rockets blast off and carry people and equipment into space.

DISCOVERY FACT™

A **moped** can't go as
fast as a motorcycle.

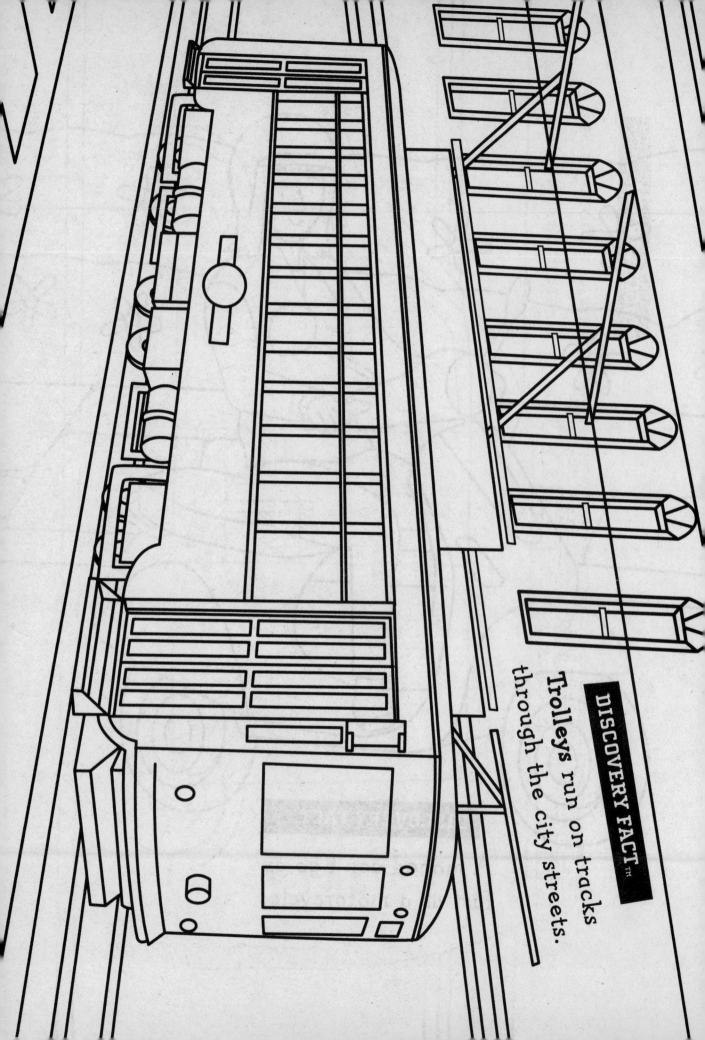

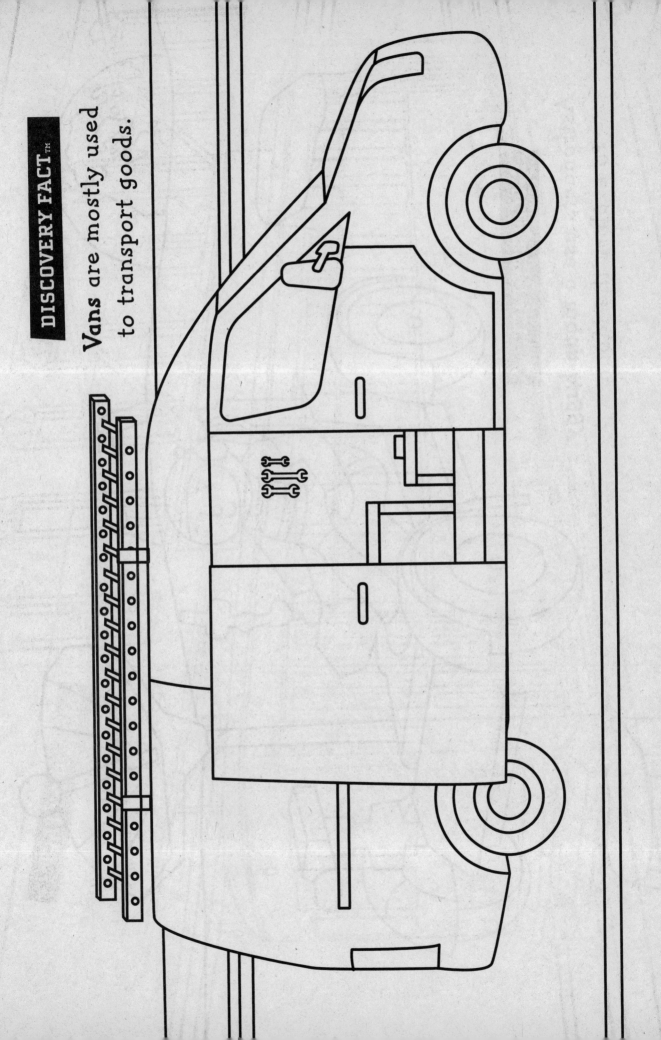

Vans are mostly used to transport goods.

DISCOVERY FACT™

Astronauts use a moon buggy
to explore the Moon.

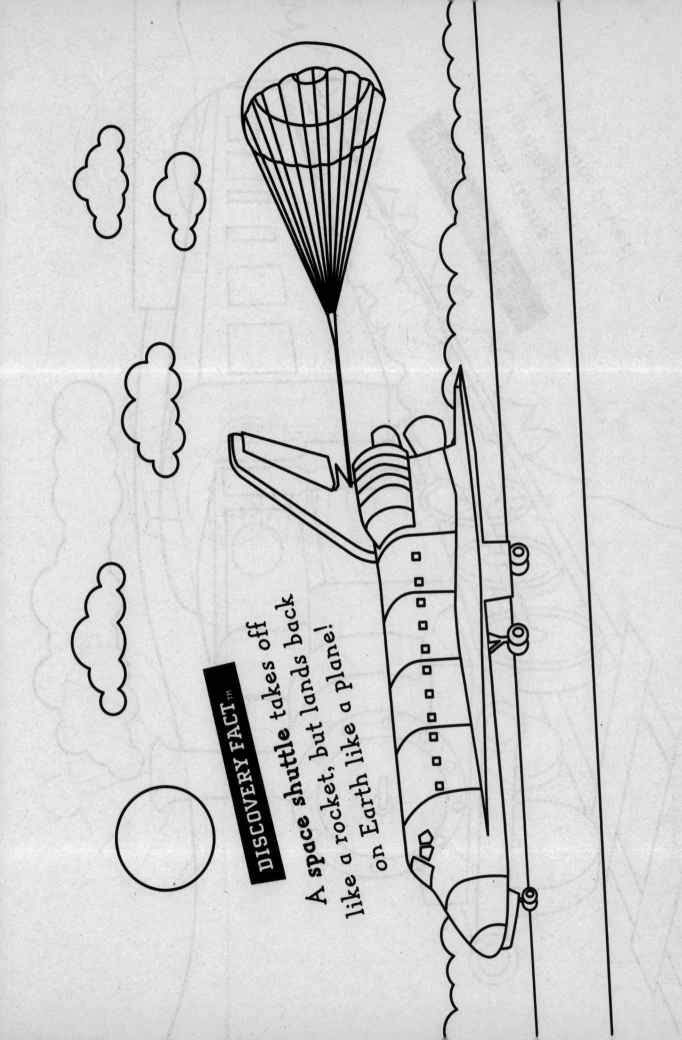

DISCOVERY FACT™

A space shuttle takes off like a rocket, but lands back on Earth like a plane!

DISCOVERY FACT™

Steam trains use burning coal to make steam power!

The first bicycle didn't have any pedals!

The first **car** traveled at 7 miles per hour—
that's about as fast as a person runs!

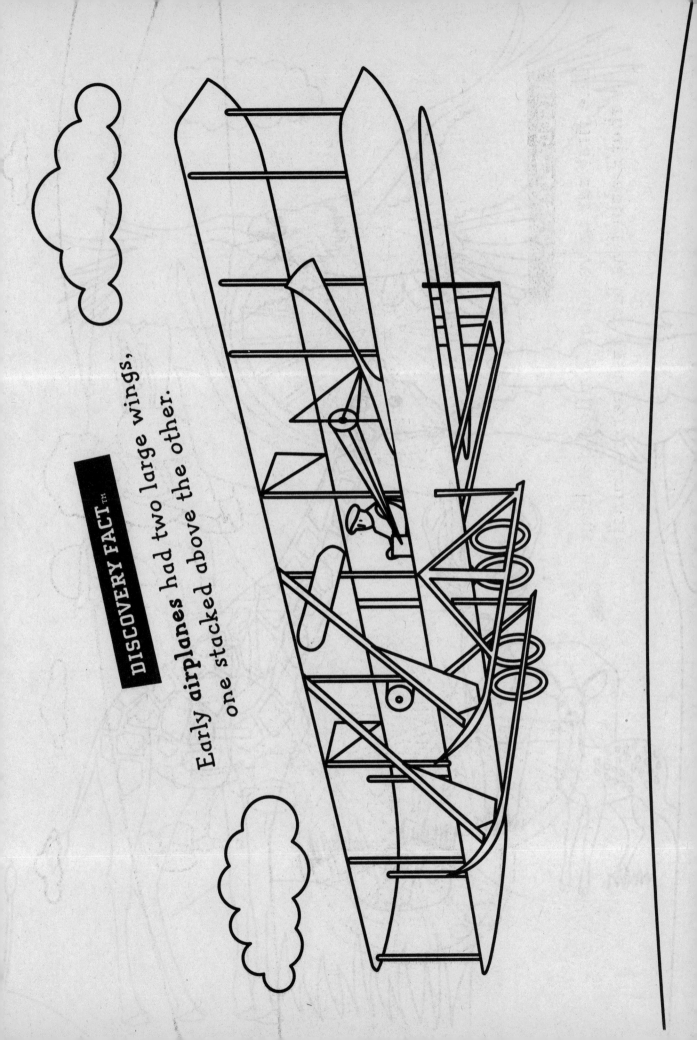

DISCOVERY FACT™

Early airplanes had two large wings, one stacked above the other.

FEATHERY BIRDS
and
AMAZING MAMMALS

DISCOVERY FACT™

The tiger is the largest wild cat in the world!

DISCOVERY FACT™

An elephant's trunk is used for smelling, grasping food, hugging, and squirting water.

DISCOVERY FACT™

Pandas can
eat more than
500 bamboo
stems a day!

A lion's roar can be heard from as far as 5 miles away.

DISCOVERY FACT™

A cow chews cud (partly digested grass) for up to 8 hours each day.

Gorillas have arms that are longer than their legs!

DISCOVERY FACT™

A rhinoceros's horns are made from the same tough stuff as our fingernails.

Cats are one of the most popular pets in the world.

Orangutans like to eat big, spiky fruits called durian, which are super-stinky!

Wolf pups
love to chase,
wrestle, and play
hide-and-seek.

Kangaroos can jump forward over 22 feet—up to three times their own height!

DISCOVERY FACT™

Most **deer** are born with white spots, but they lose them within a year.

The name **hippopotamus**
means "river horse."

DISCOVERY FACT™

A **mountain goat's** hooves have rough pads on the bottom to help them climb rocky slopes.

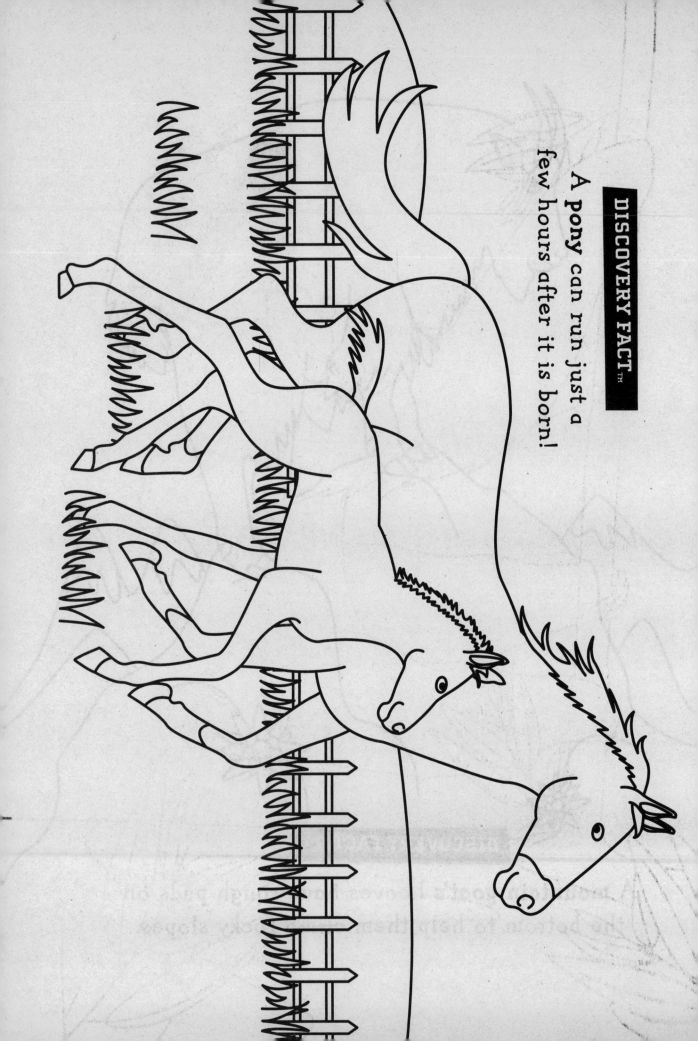

DISCOVERY FACT™

A pony can run just a few hours after it is born!

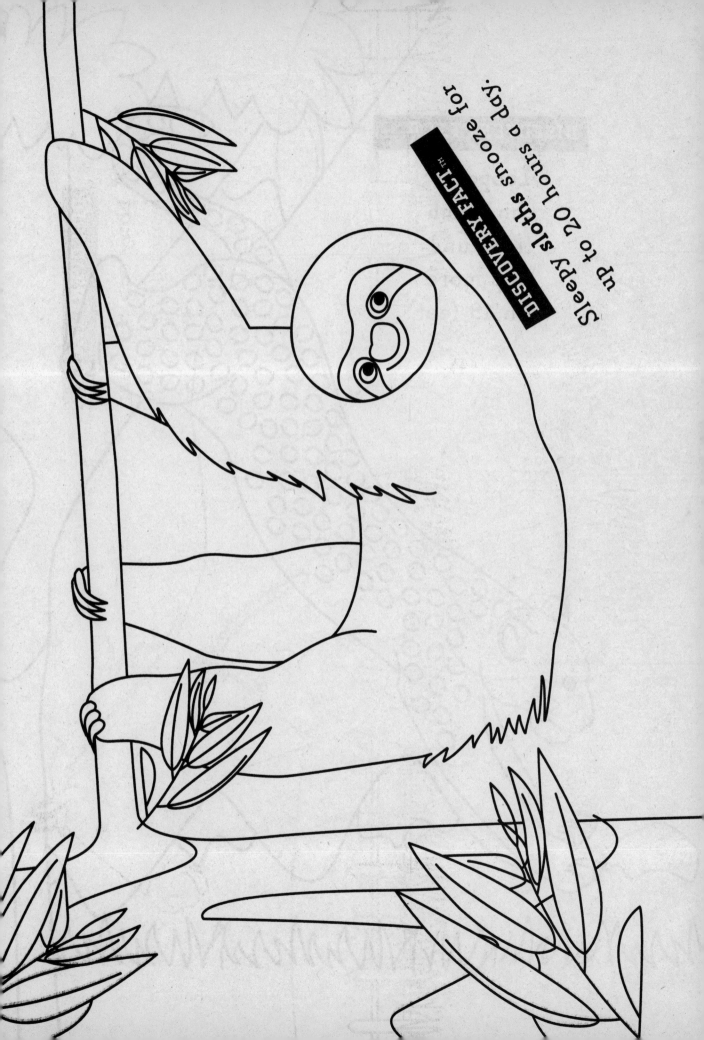

DISCOVERY FACT™

Leopards can climb trees and leap more than 19 feet.

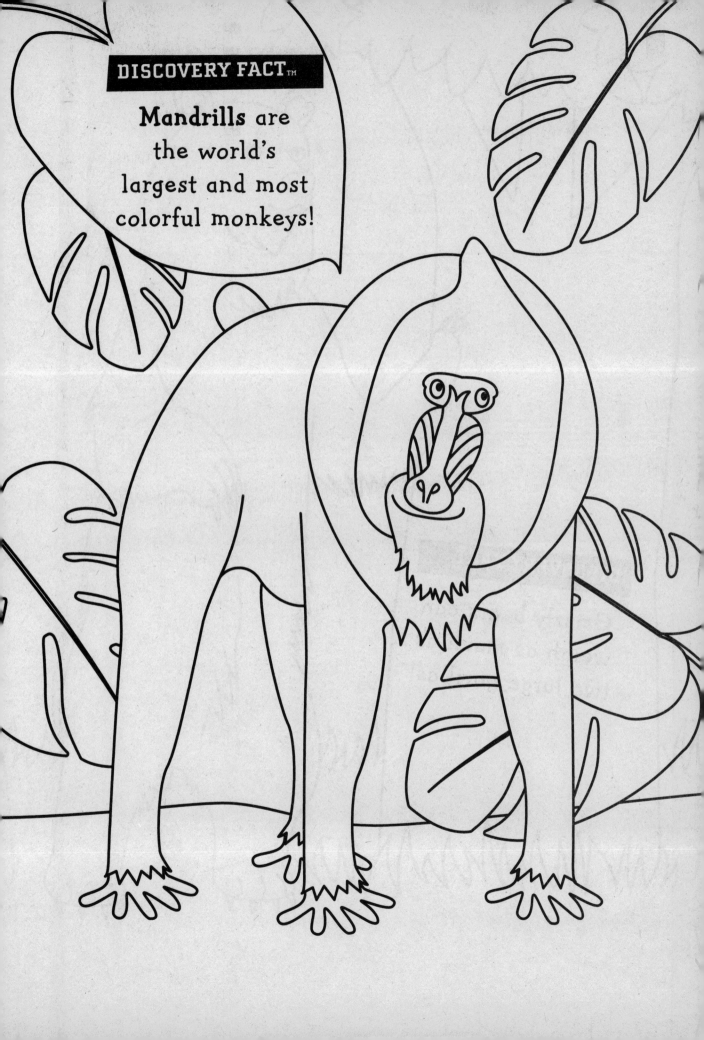

DISCOVERY FACT™

Mandrills are the world's largest and most colorful monkeys!

DISCOVERY FACT™

Grizzly bears can weigh as much as two large gorillas!

The most
popular pet
dog in the
world is
the playful
Labrador.

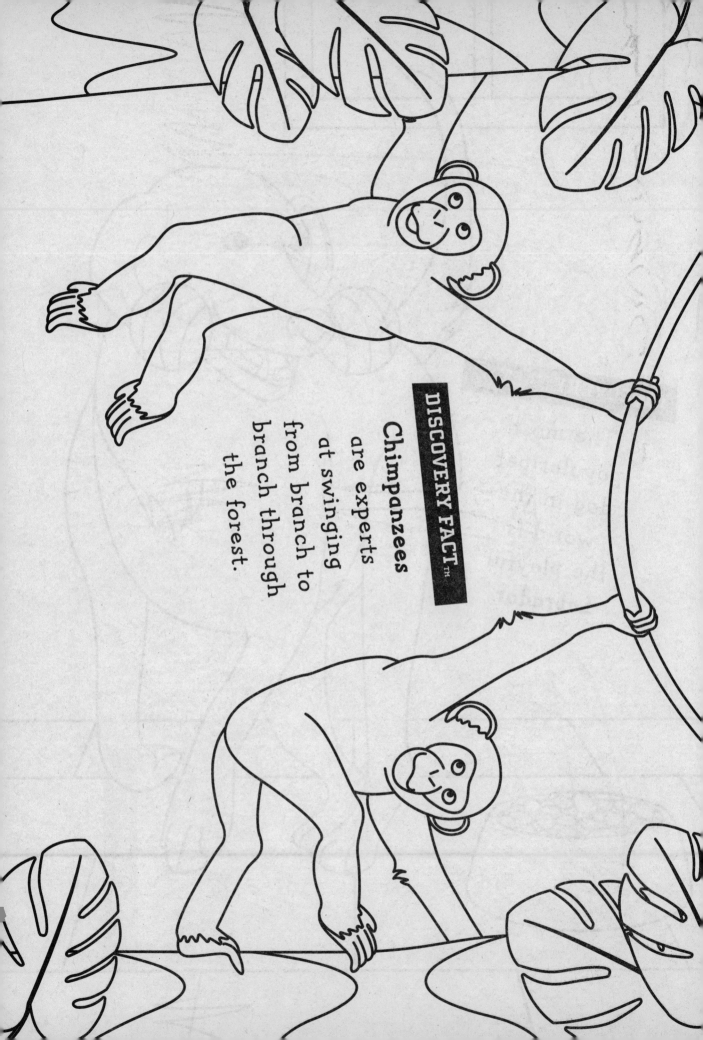

DISCOVERY FACT™

Chimpanzees
are experts
at swinging
from branch to
branch through
the forest.

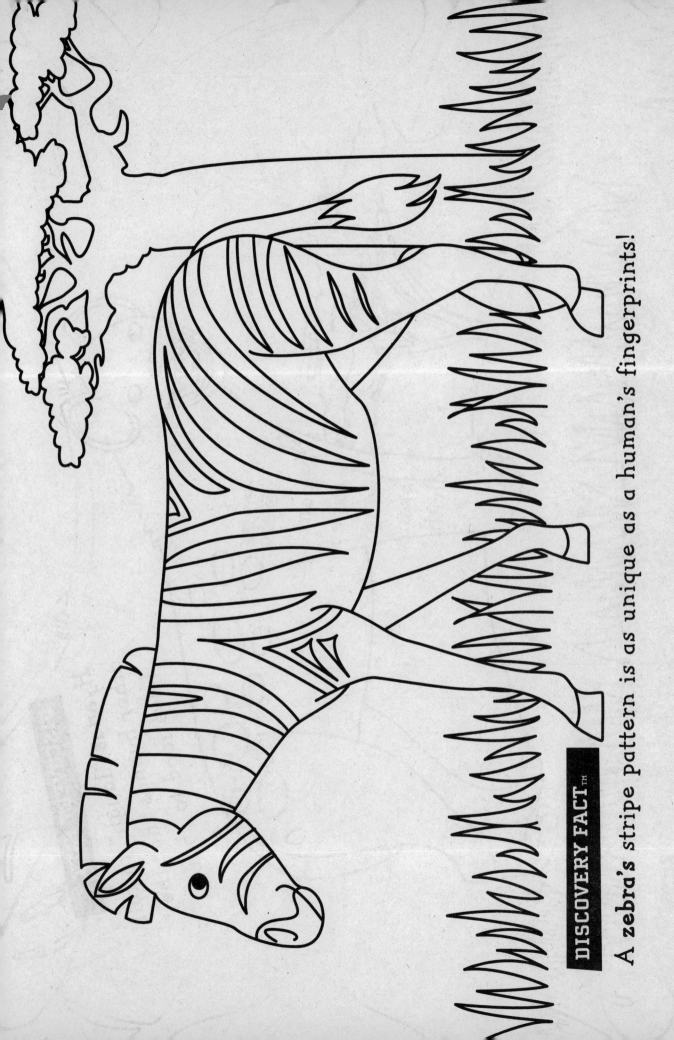

DISCOVERY FACT™

A zebra's stripe pattern is as unique as a human's fingerprints!

DISCOVERY FACT™

Hyenas "laugh" to tell other hyenas that they have food to share.

Raccoons have a black fur "mask" across their eyes.

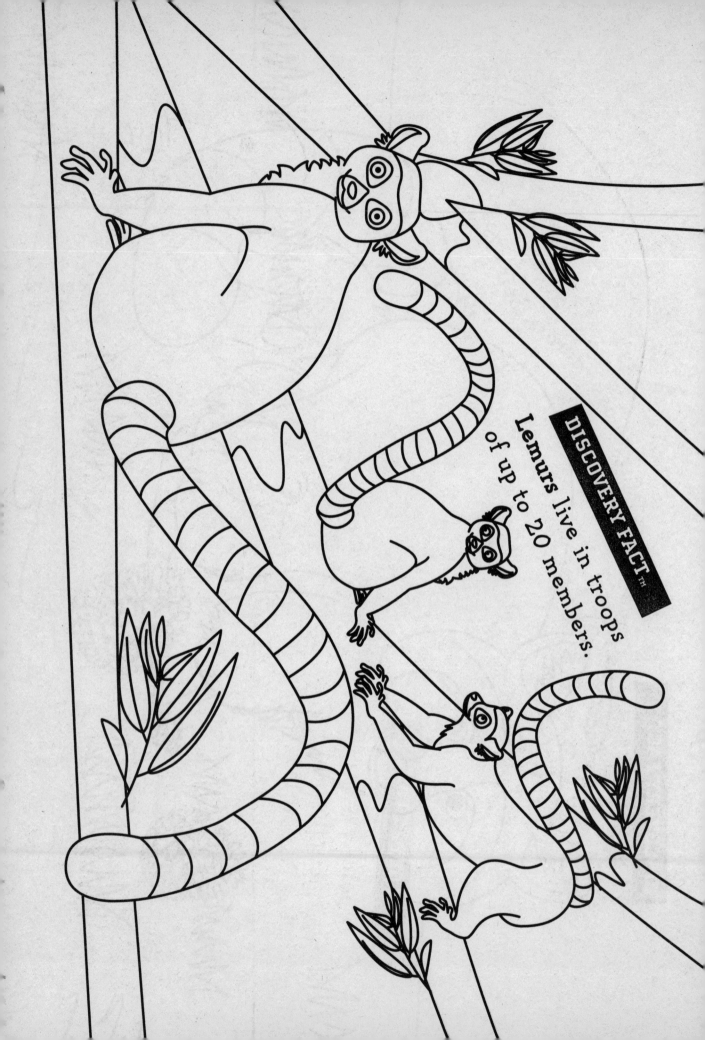

DISCOVERY FACT™

Lemurs live in troops of up to 20 members.

DISCOVERY FACT™

A polar bear's hair isn't actually white— it is colorless!

DISCOVERY FACT™

If a **skunk** feels threatened, it sprays a stinky musk from near its tail!

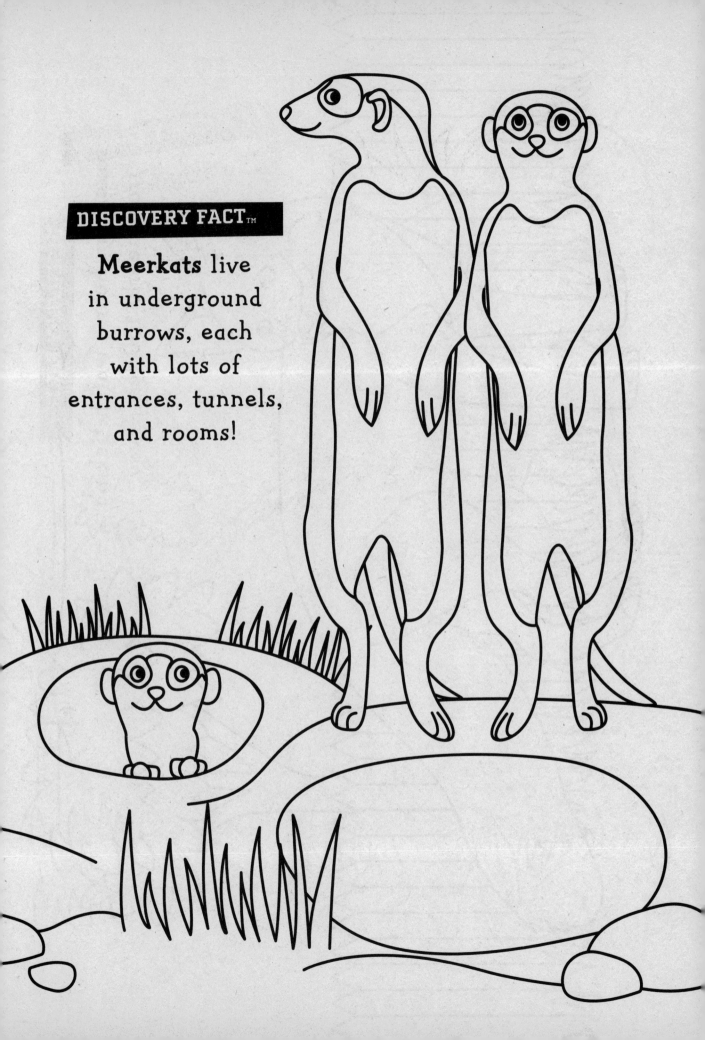

DISCOVERY FACT™

Meerkats live in underground burrows, each with lots of entrances, tunnels, and rooms!

Foxes can hear a watch ticking from nearly 130 feet away.

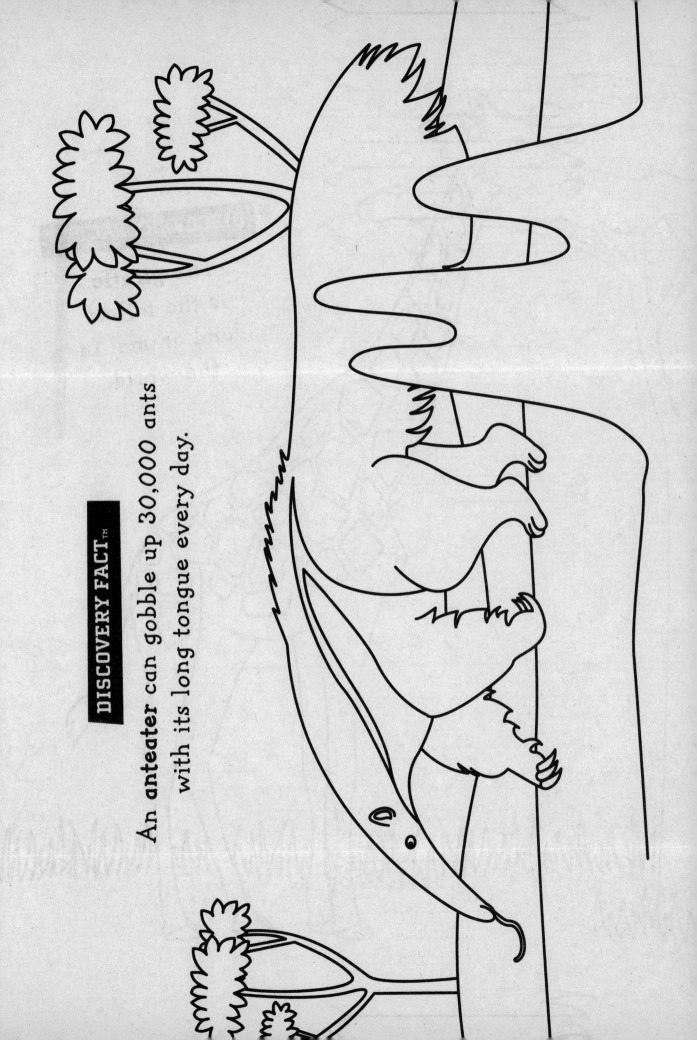

DISCOVERY FACT™

An anteater can gobble up 30,000 ants with its long tongue every day.

DISCOVERY FACT™

The **giraffe** is the tallest land animal in the world.

DISCOVERY FACT™

Like kangaroos, **koalas** carry their babies in a pouch.

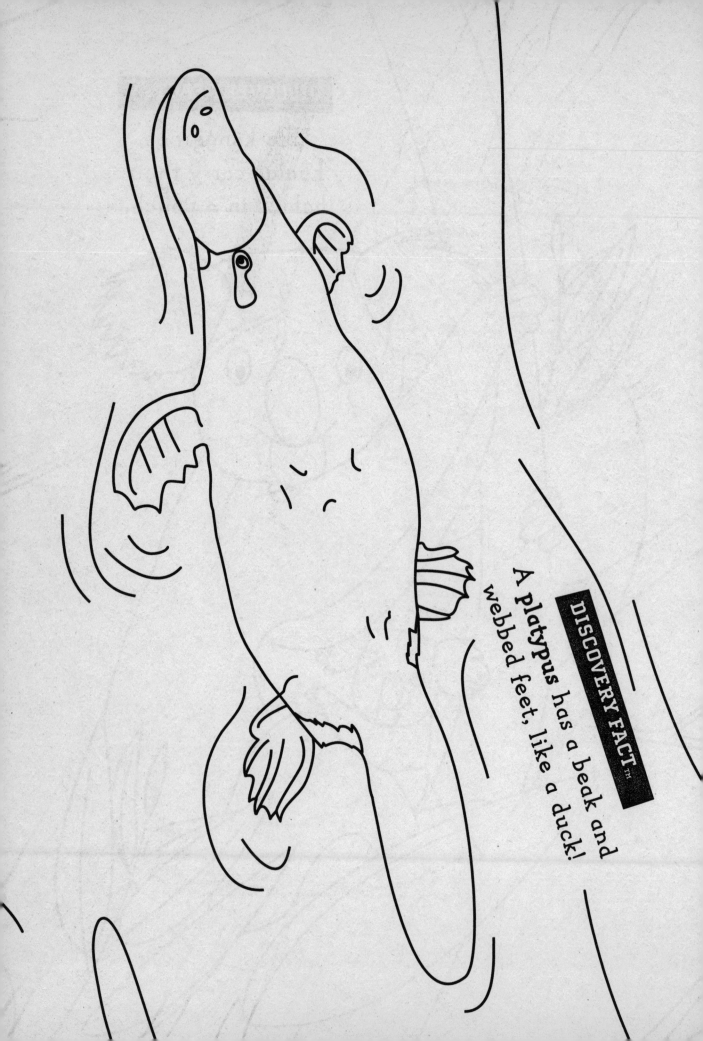

DISCOVERY FACT™

A platypus has a beak and webbed feet, like a duck!

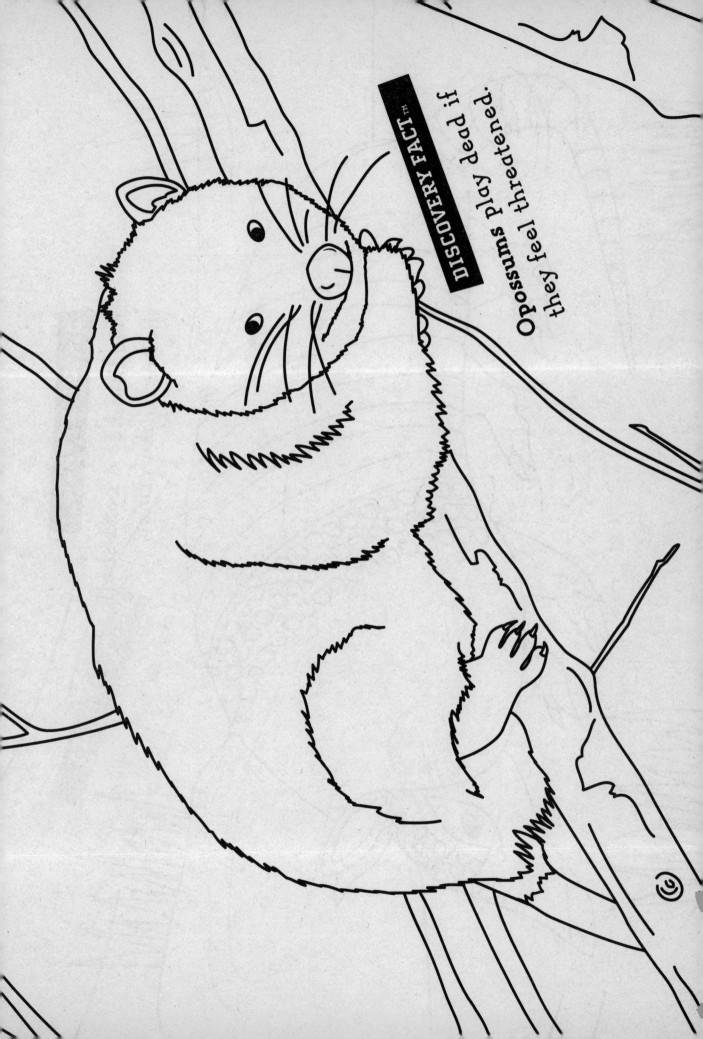

DISCOVERY FACT™

Opossums play dead if they feel threatened.

DISCOVERY FACT™

The **armadillo** has a hard shell that acts like armor.

DISCOVERY FACT™

Most golden lion tamarins are twins!

DISCOVERY FACT™

Hares are larger than rabbits, and they have longer ears.

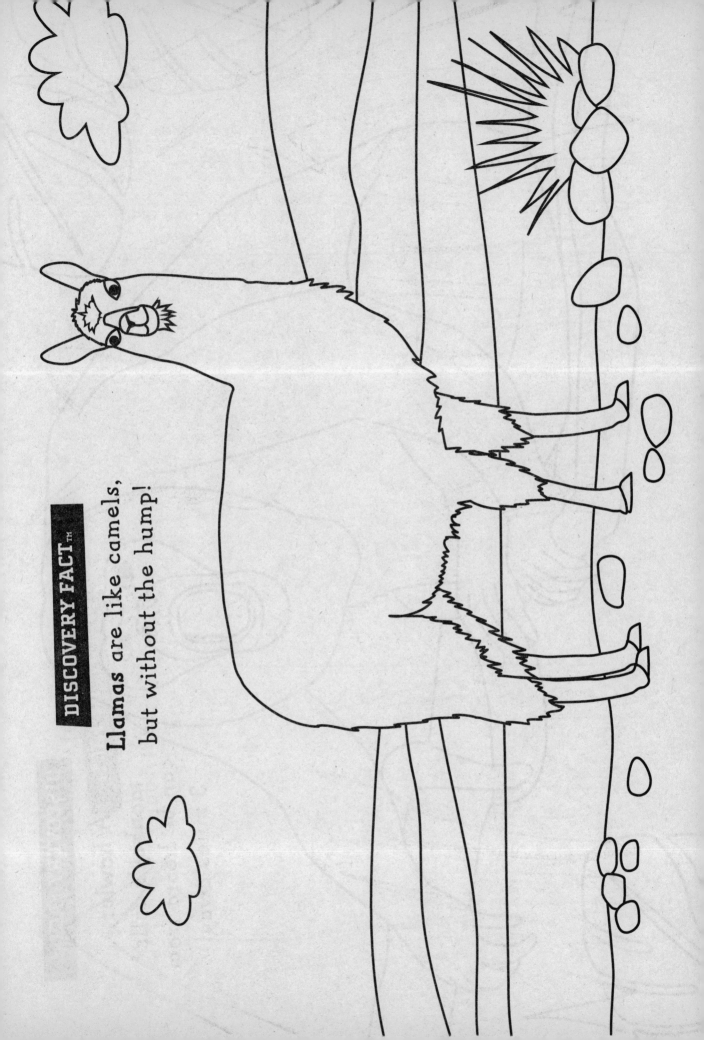

DISCOVERY FACT™

Llamas are like camels, but without the hump!

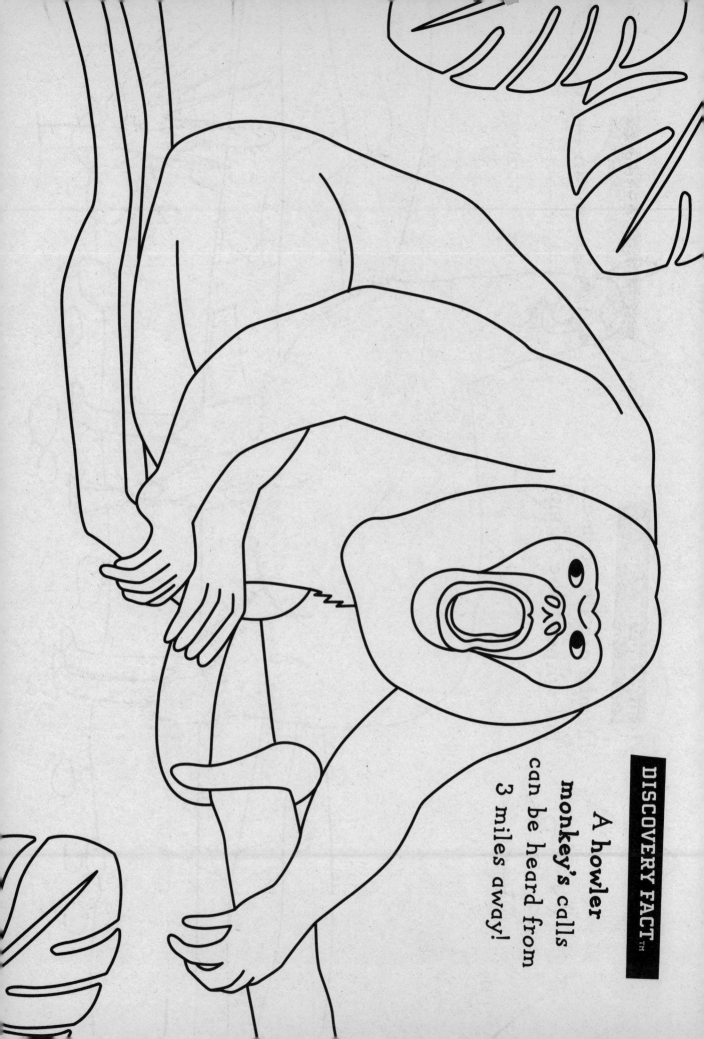

DISCOVERY FACT™

A howler monkey's calls can be heard from 3 miles away!

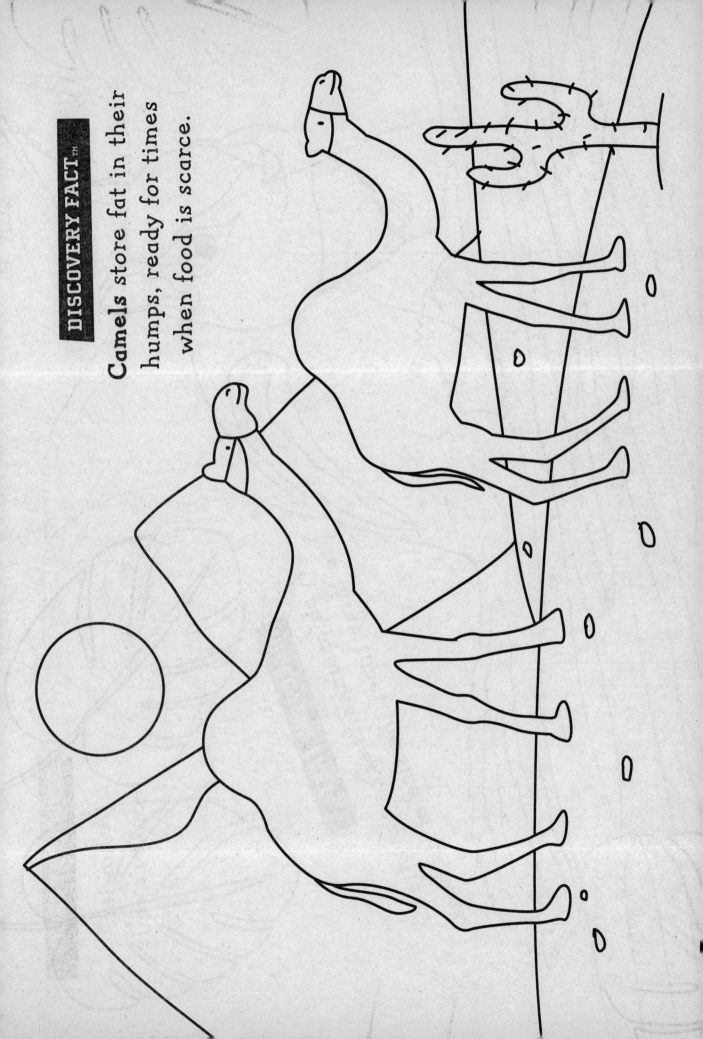

Camels store fat in their humps, ready for times when food is scarce.

DISCOVERY FACT™

A chipmunk's cheeks can stretch to three times the size of its head!

DISCOVERY FACT™

Flying squirrels use their stretchy skin like a parachute to glide through the air.

DISCOVERY FACT™

A moose's antlers help
channel sound into its ears.

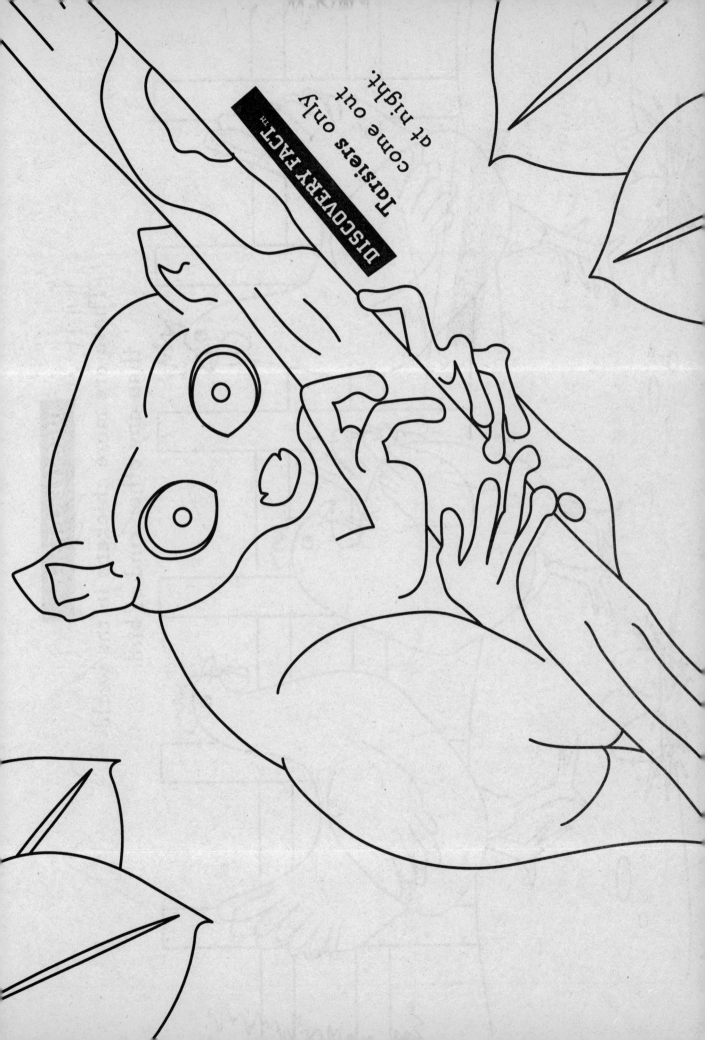

DISCOVERY FACT™

Tarsiers only come out at night.

There are more chickens in the world than any other kind of bird.

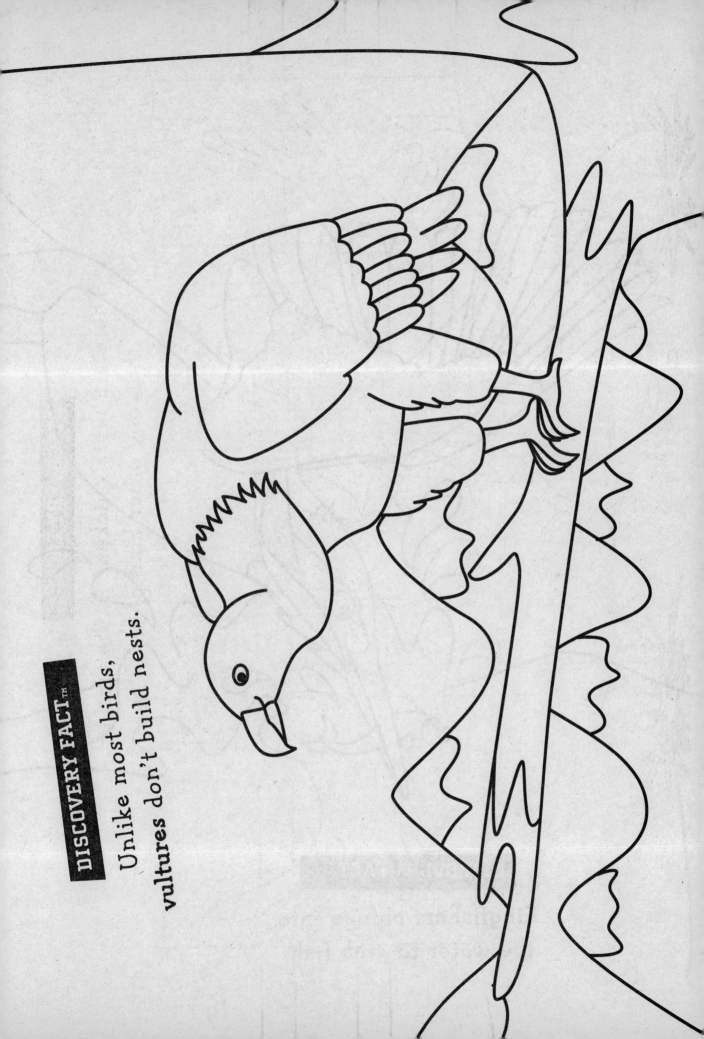

DISCOVERY FACT™

Unlike most birds, vultures don't build nests.

DISCOVERY FACT™

Kingfishers plunge into
the water to grab fish.

DISCOVERY FACT™

Pheasants eat a mixture of berries, seeds, young shoots, and insects.

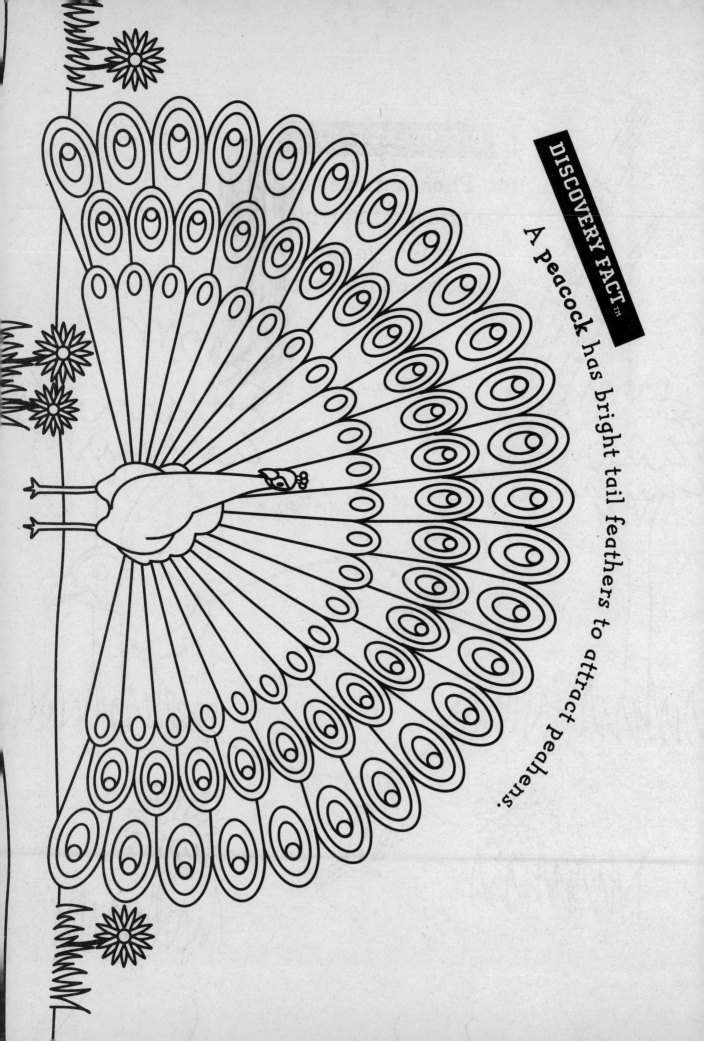

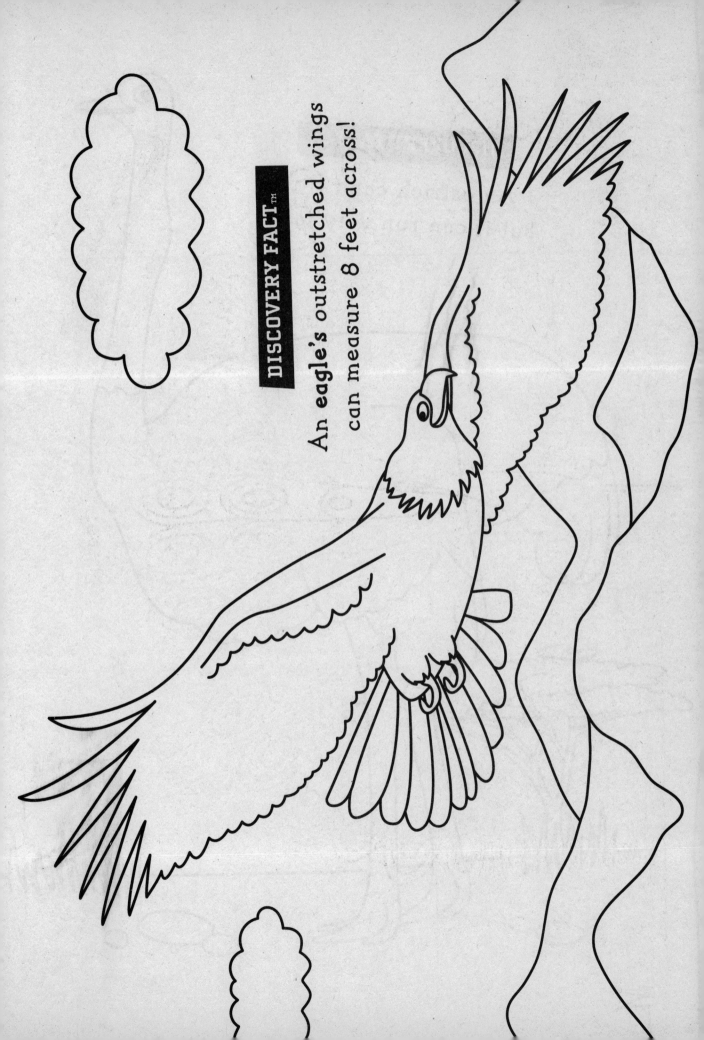

DISCOVERY FACT™

An **eagle's** outstretched wings can measure 8 feet across!

An **ostrich** can't fly,
but it can run very fast!

DISCOVERY FACT™

A **toucan's** huge colorful beak is one-third of the length of its body!

DISCOVERY FACT™

An **owl** can turn its head almost the whole way around.

DISCOVERY FACT™

The **African gray parrot** can copy human speech!

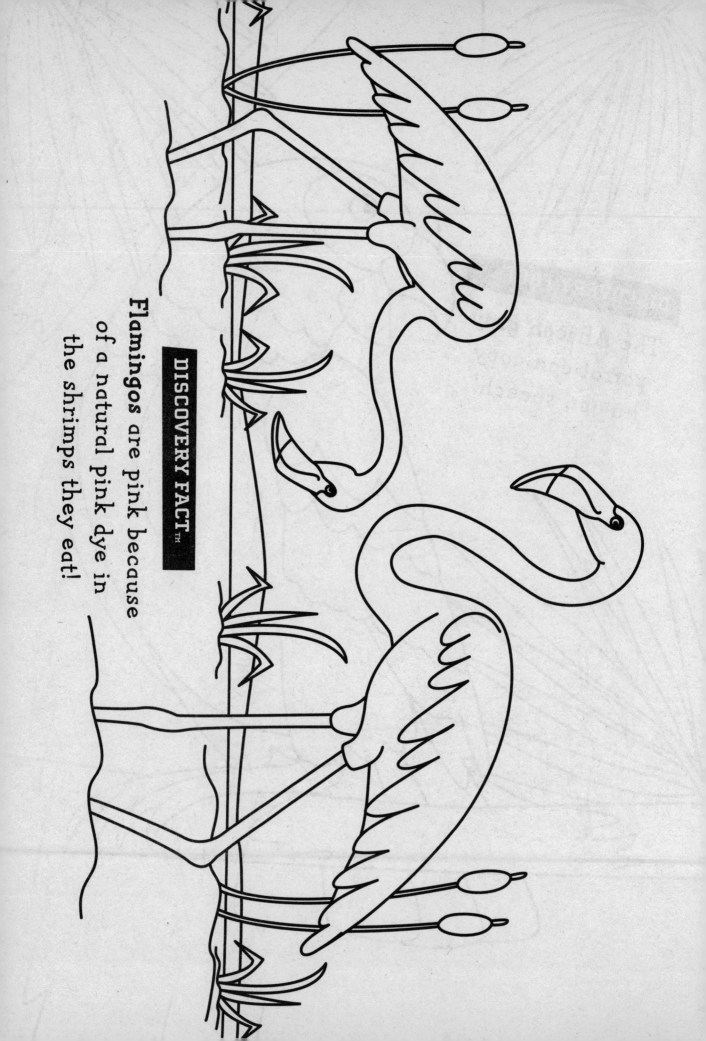

DISCOVERY FACT™

Flamingos are pink because of a natural pink dye in the shrimps they eat!

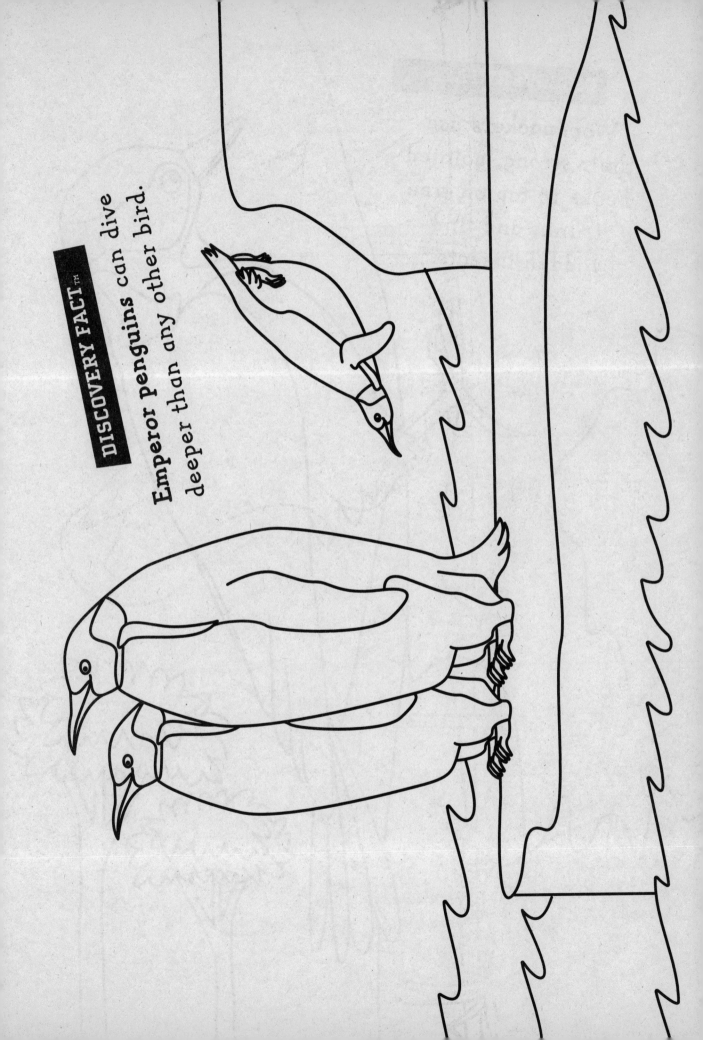

DISCOVERY FACT ™

Emperor penguins can dive deeper than any other bird.

Woodpeckers use their strong, pointed beaks to tap on tree trunks and find hidden insects.

DISCOVERY FACT™

Swans are the largest flying
birds in the world!

DISCOVERY FACT™

Hummingbirds flap their wings so fast that they make a humming noise.

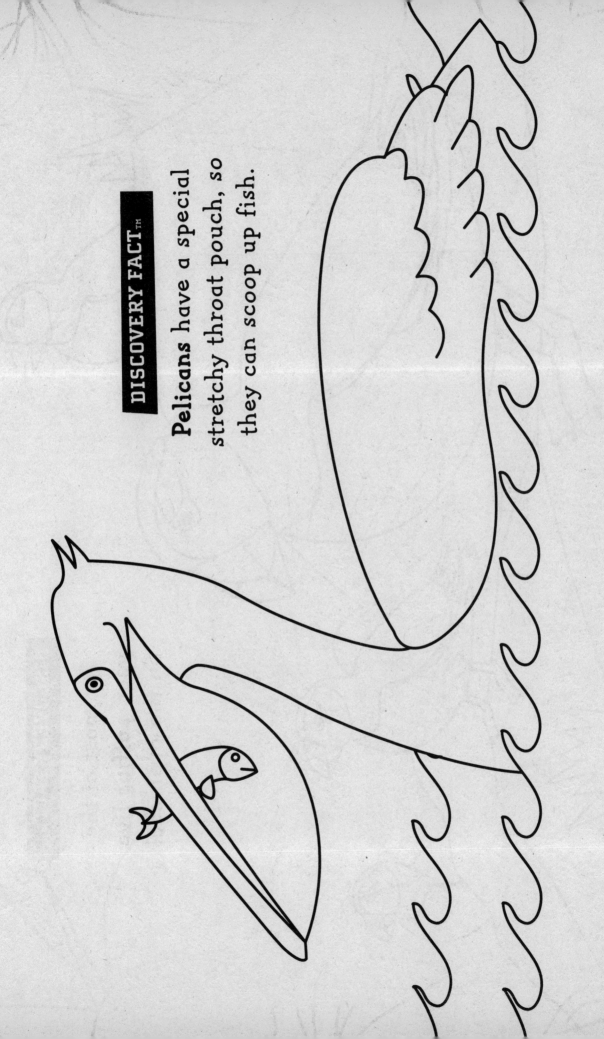

DISCOVERY FACT™

Pelicans have a special stretchy throat pouch, so they can scoop up fish.

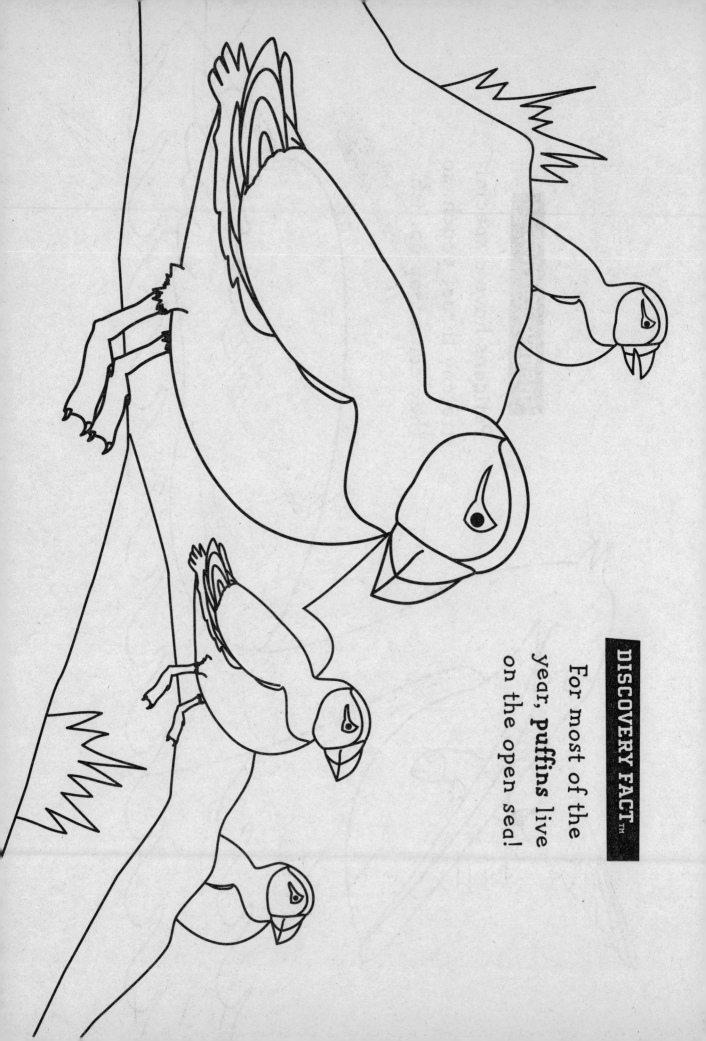

For most of the year, **puffins** live on the open sea!

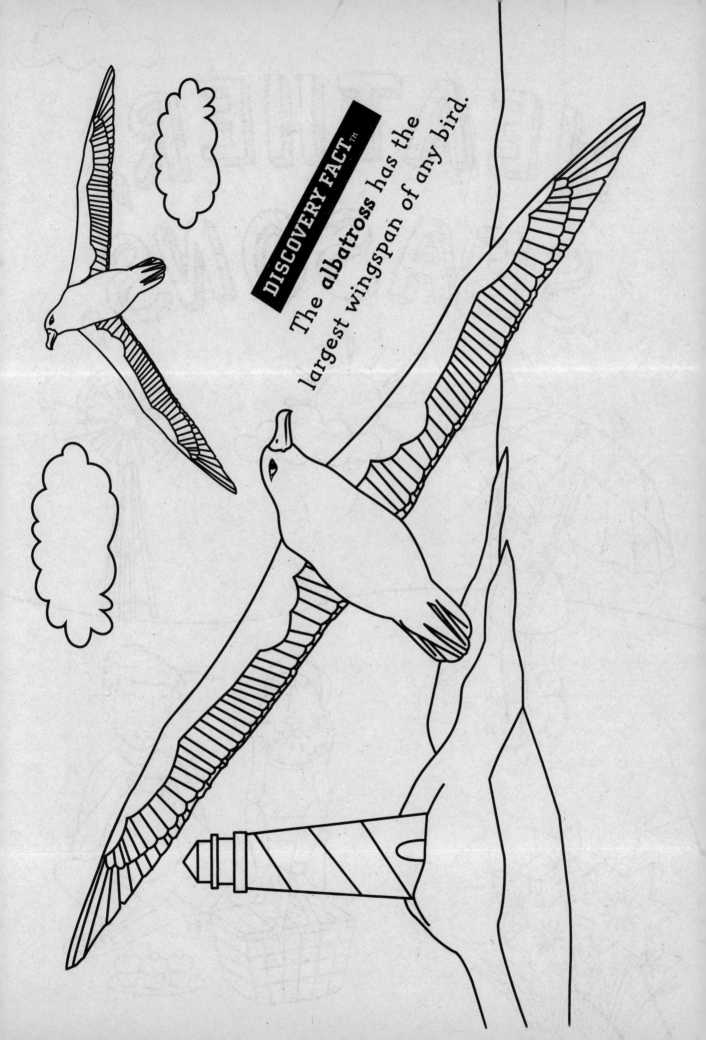

DISCOVERY FACT™

The albatross has the largest wingspan of any bird.

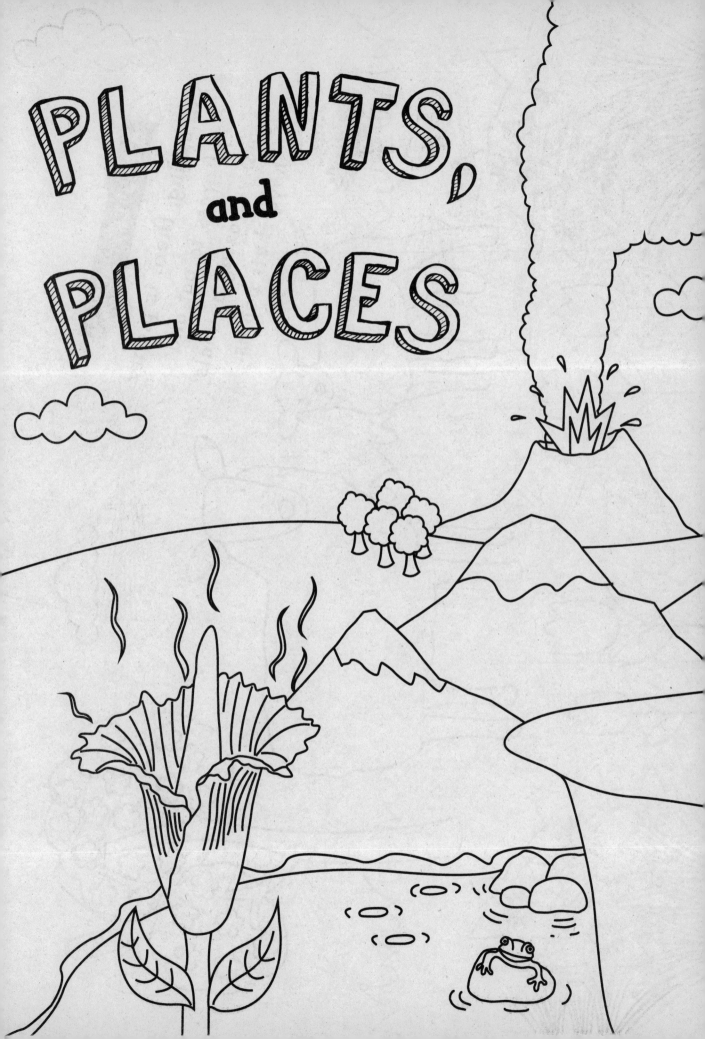

DISCOVERY FACT™

In **spring**, there is plenty of grass to eat and many grazing animals have their babies.

DISCOVERY FACT™

Summer has the longest and warmest days of the year.

Winter has the shortest and coldest days of the year.

Wind blows at different speeds, from a slow and gentle breeze to a fast and furious hurricane.

DISCOVERY FACT™

Some **rain drops** are tiny;
others are half an inch long.

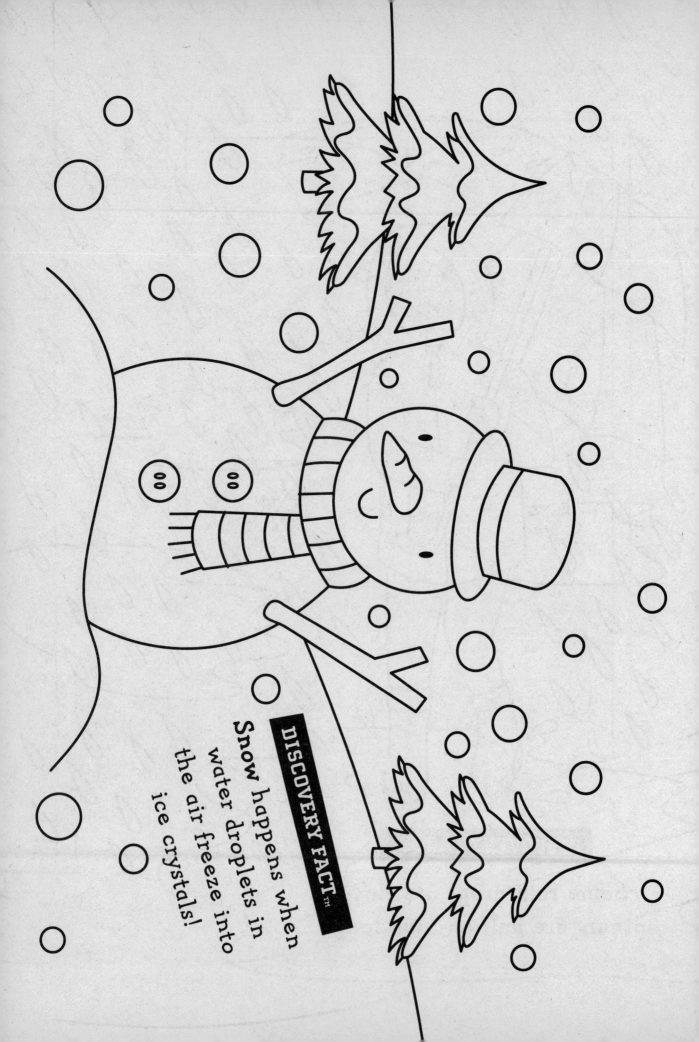

DISCOVERY FACT™

Snow happens when water droplets in the air freeze into ice crystals!

DISCOVERY FACT™

During a **thunderstorm**, lightning flashes and makes the sound of thunder.

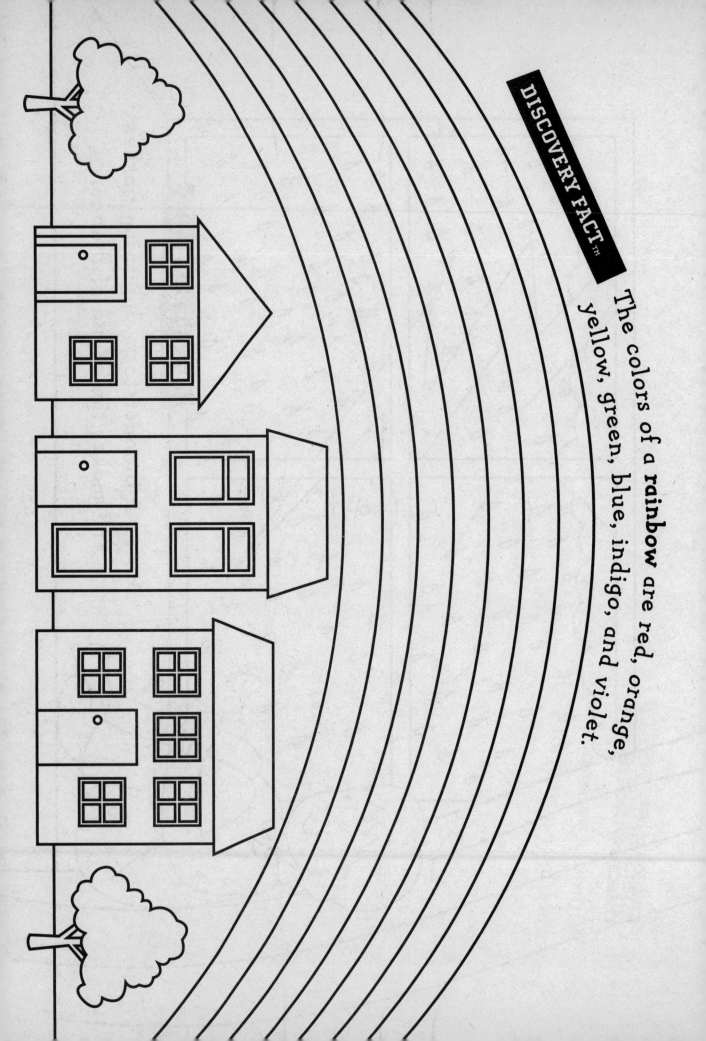

The colors of a **rainbow** are red, orange, yellow, green, blue, indigo, and violet.

DISCOVERY FACT™

Without the **Sun**, there would be no heat or light!

DISCOVERY FACT™

Volcanoes sometimes spew out molten lava, hot ash, and gas.

DISCOVERY FACT™

Some of the
largest lakes
can be seen
from space!

DISCOVERY FACT™

Caves are nature's underground chambers and tunnels.

Ponds can give frogs and fish a home.

DISCOVERY FACT™

Mountains are large hills
more than 2,000 feet tall.

DISCOVERY FACT™

The Nile River is the longest **river** in the world.

DISCOVERY FACT™

Geysers shoot hot water and steam up into the air!

DISCOVERY FACT™

Streams are
like small,
narrow rivers!

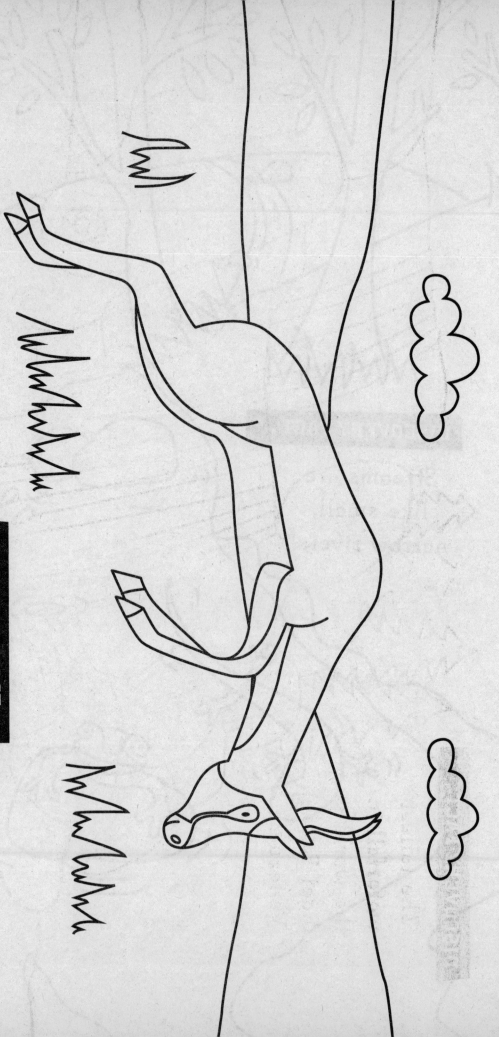

DISCOVERY FACT™

Grazing animals, such as gazelles, live in **grasslands**.

The tallest **waterfall** in the world is Angel Falls in Venezuela.

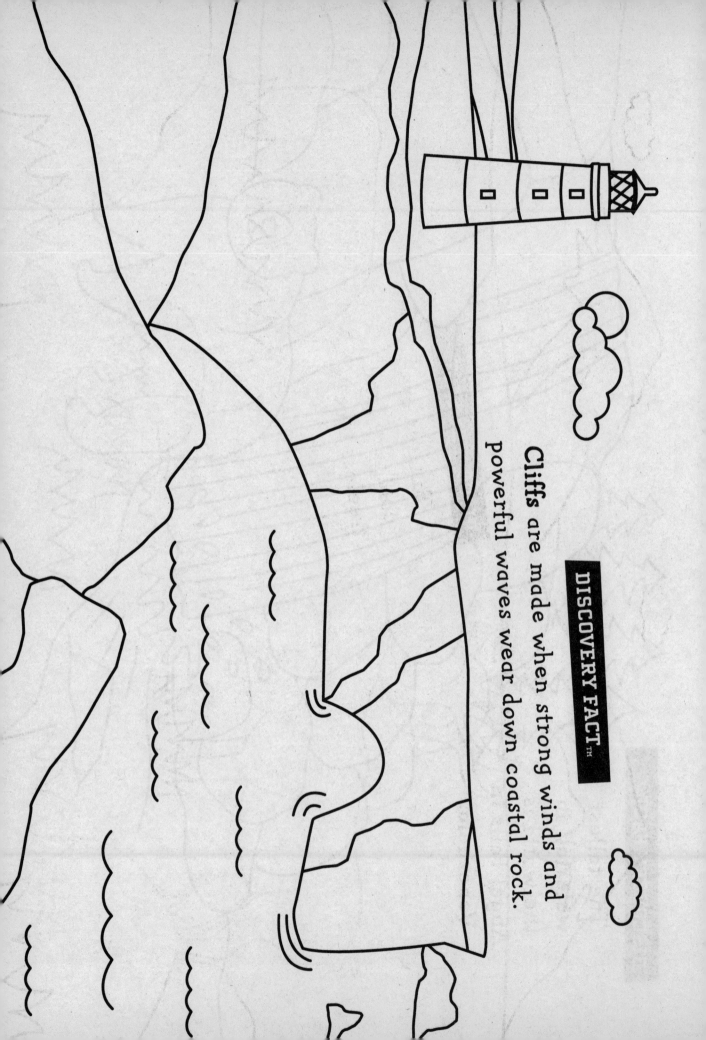

DISCOVERY FACT™

Cliffs are made when strong winds and powerful waves wear down coastal rock.

DISCOVERY FACT™

Tundras are cold, flat, and treeless places.

DISCOVERY FACT ™

Tropical rain forests
are hot, rainy, and
full of animals,
plants, and trees.

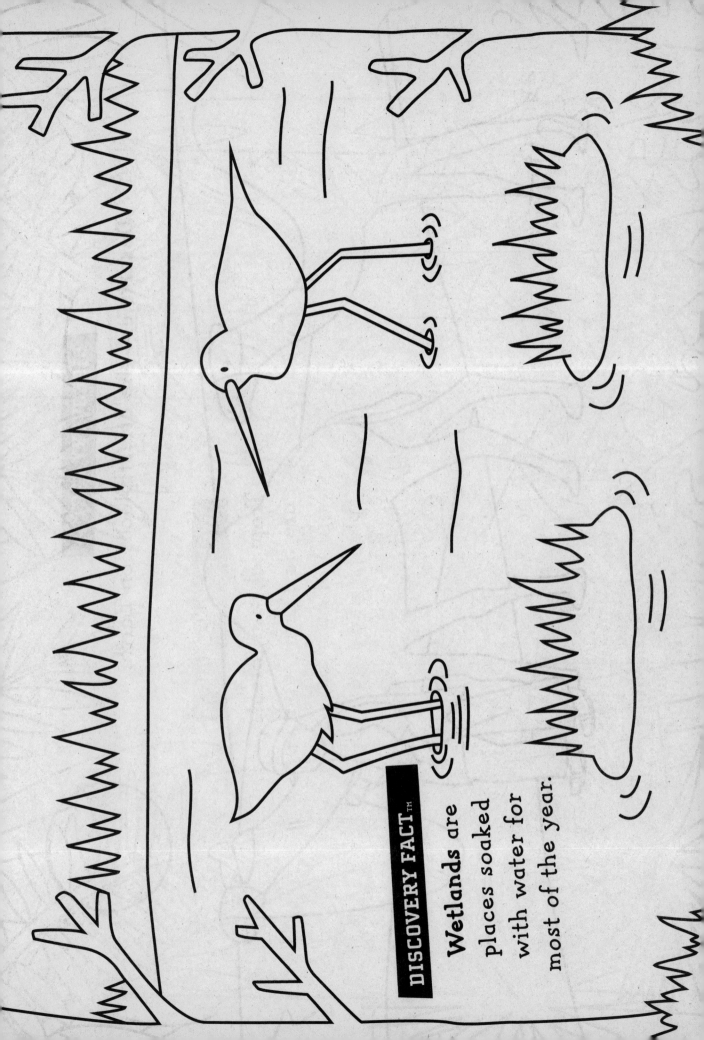

DISCOVERY FACT™

Wetlands are places soaked with water for most of the year.

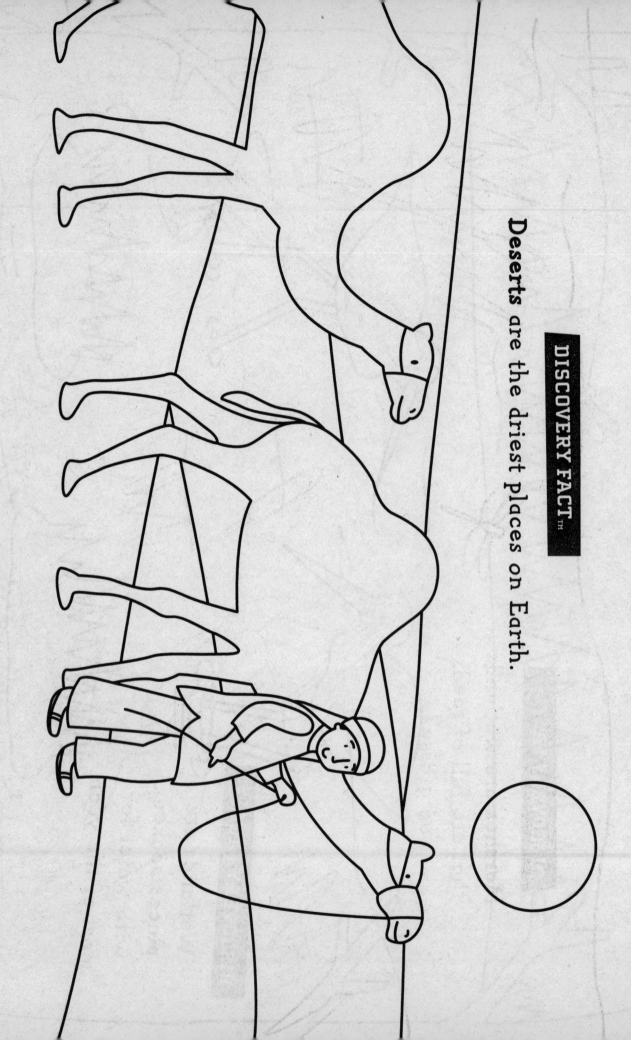

DISCOVERY FACT™

Deserts are the driest places on Earth.

DISCOVERY FACT™

Marshes are wetlands that are full of reeds and grasses.

DISCOVERY FACT™

Jungles have
lots of plants on
the ground.

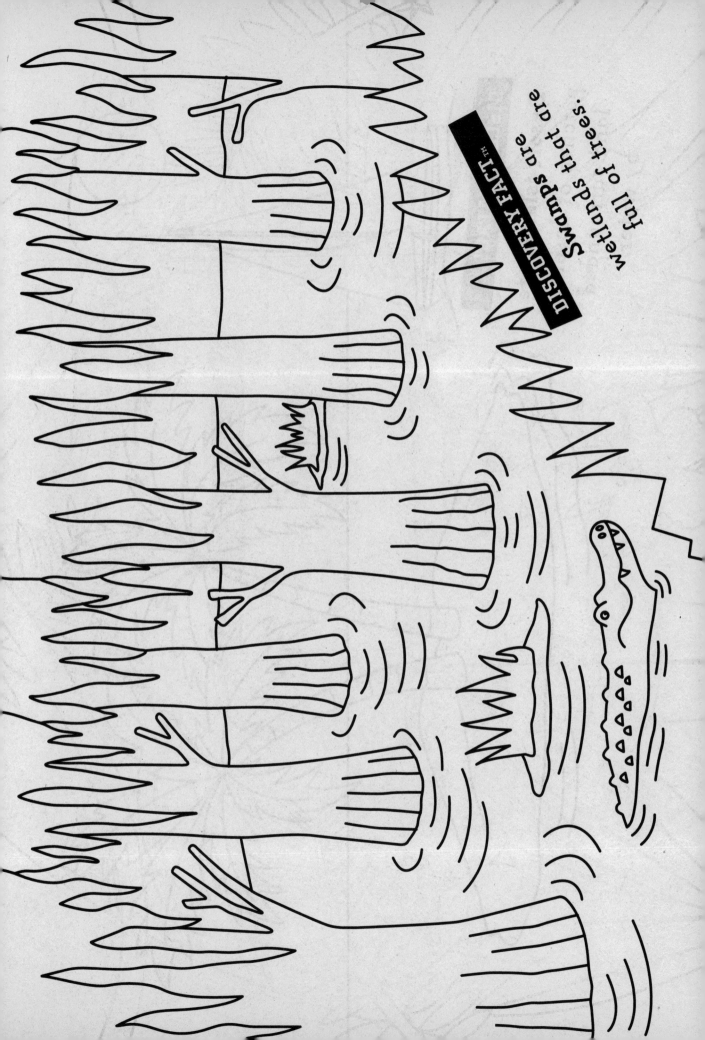

DISCOVERY FACT™

Swamps are wetlands that are full of trees.

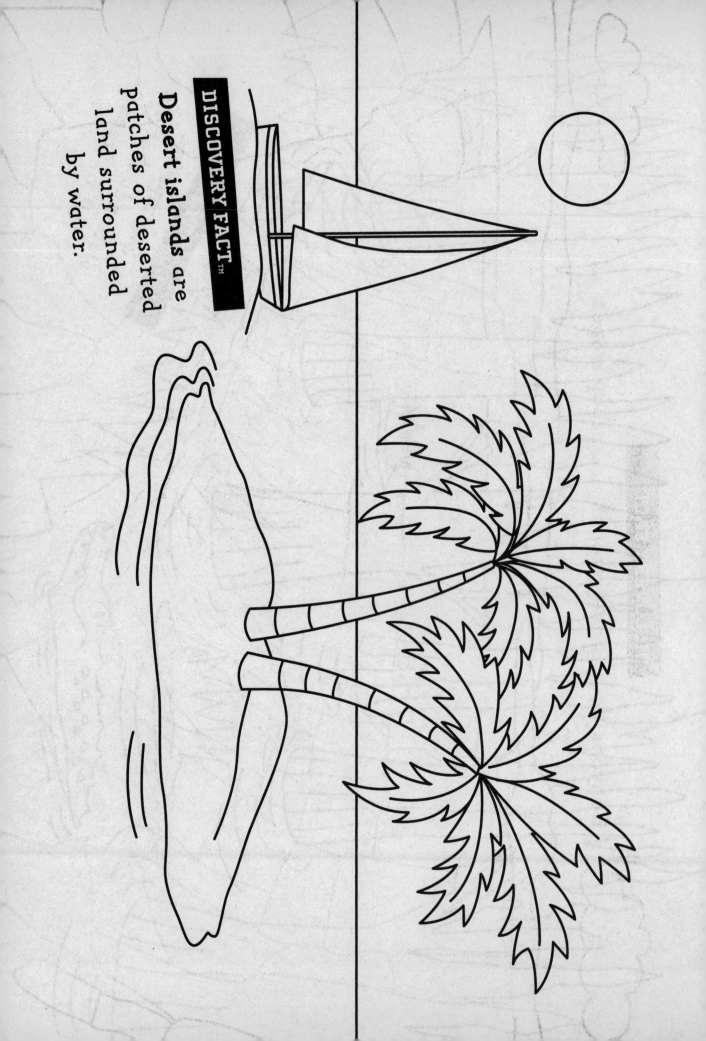

DISCOVERY FACT™

Desert islands are patches of deserted land surrounded by water.

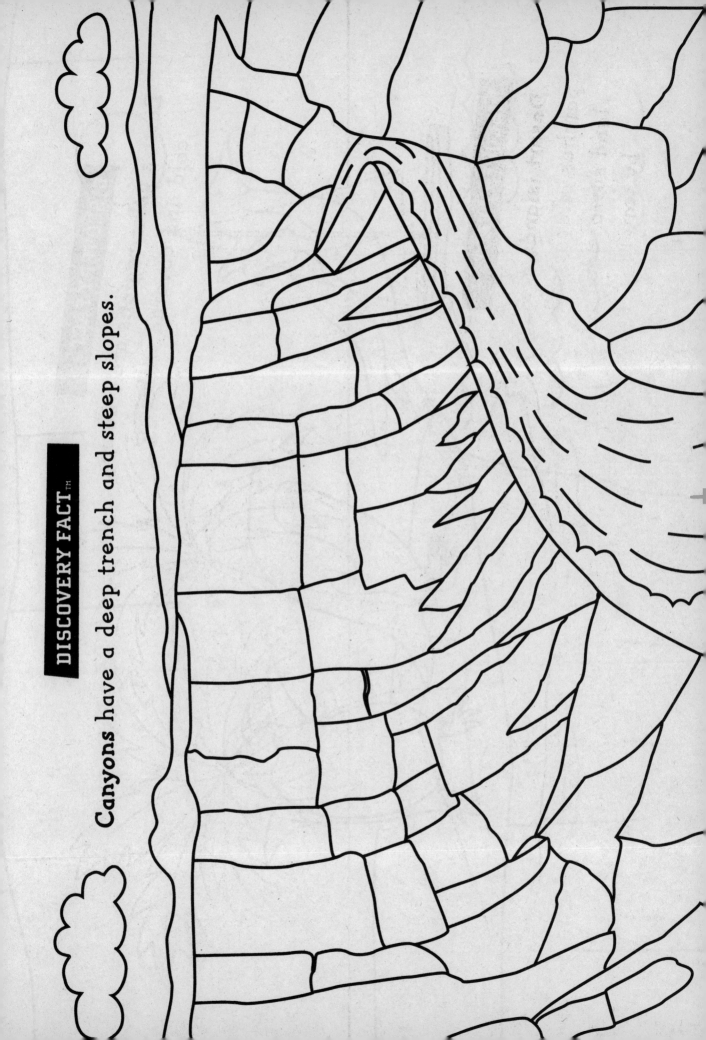

Canyons have a deep trench and steep slopes.

DISCOVERY FACT™

Earth's polar regions are freezing cold and covered with ice.

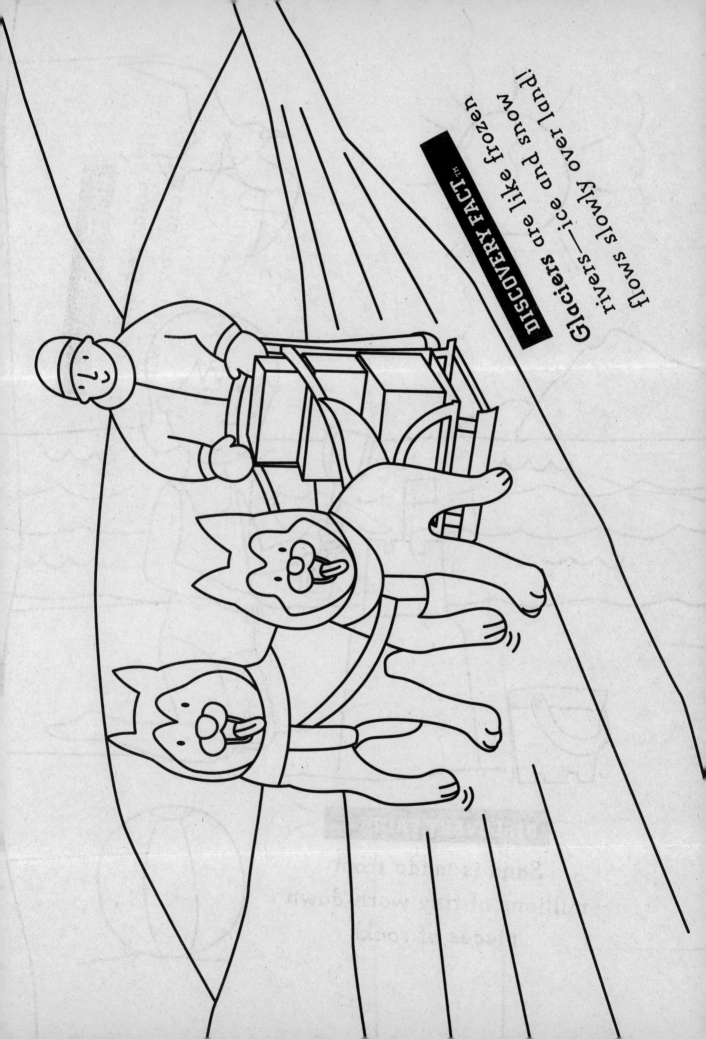

DISCOVERY FACT™

Glaciers are like frozen rivers—ice and snow flows slowly over land!

DISCOVERY FACT™

Sand is made from millions of tiny worn-down pieces of rock!

DISCOVERY FACT™

Valleys are found between slopes or hills.

DISCOVERY FACT™

Sand **dunes** can be shaped and moved by the wind.

On **rocky shores**, some creatures, such as starfish, anchor themselves to the rocks.

DISCOVERY FACT™

Coral reefs are like underwater forests— they are full of color!

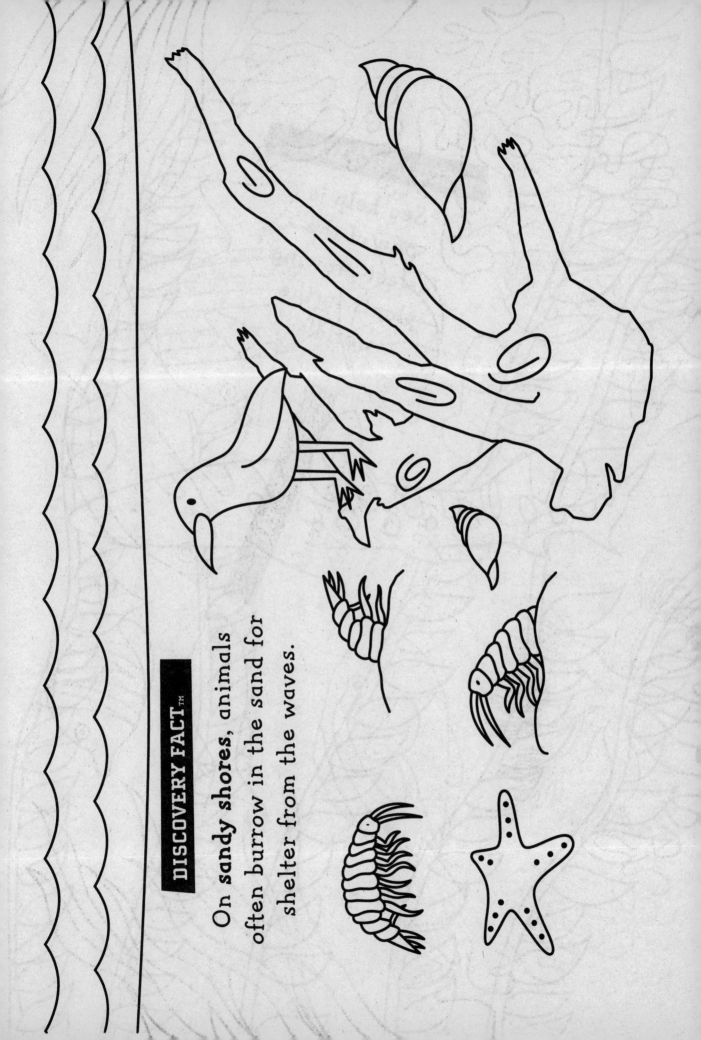

DISCOVERY FACT ™

On sandy shores, animals often burrow in the sand for shelter from the waves.

DISCOVERY FACT™

Sea kelp is one of the fastest-growing plants in the world!

DISCOVERY FACT™

Seagrass meadows grow under the sea.

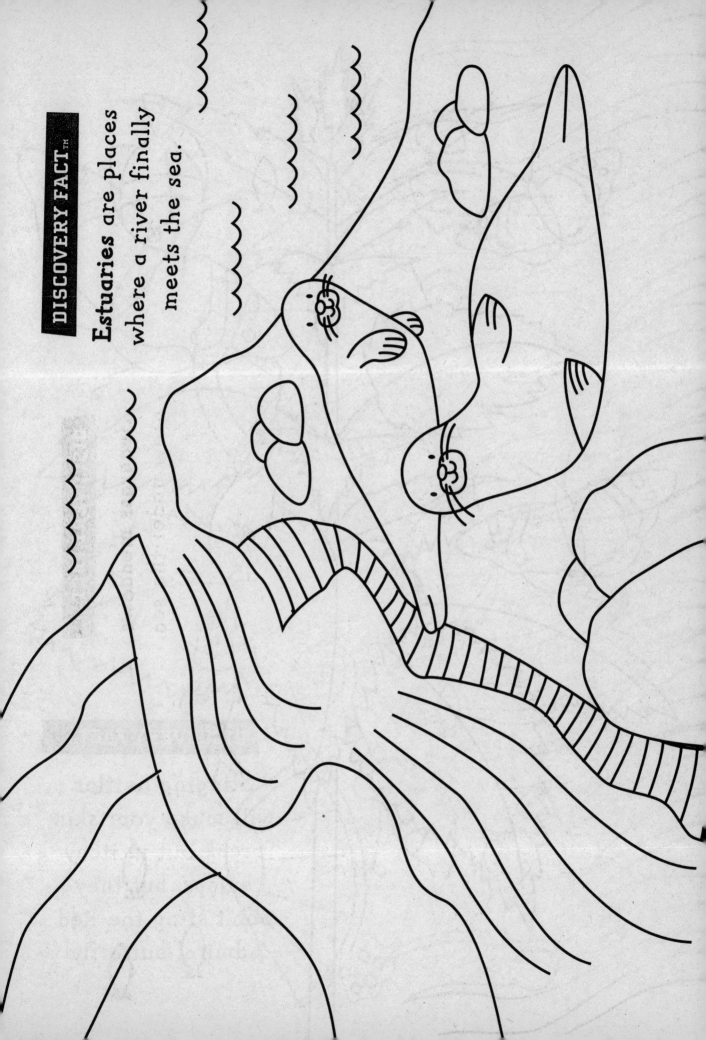

DISCOVERY FACT™

Estuaries are places where a river finally meets the sea.

DISCOVERY FACT™

Stinging nettles
will make your skin
break out in itchy
bumps, but they
don't sting the Red
Admiral butterfly!

DISCOVERY FACT™

Some **roses** smell
so nice that
they are used to
make perfume.

DISCOVERY FACT ™

A giant water lily can grow almost 10 feet wide!

Sunflowers have large golden flowers.

The **corpse flower** is the world's smelliest plant—it smells like rotting meat!

Venus flytraps trap insects by snapping their leaves shut.

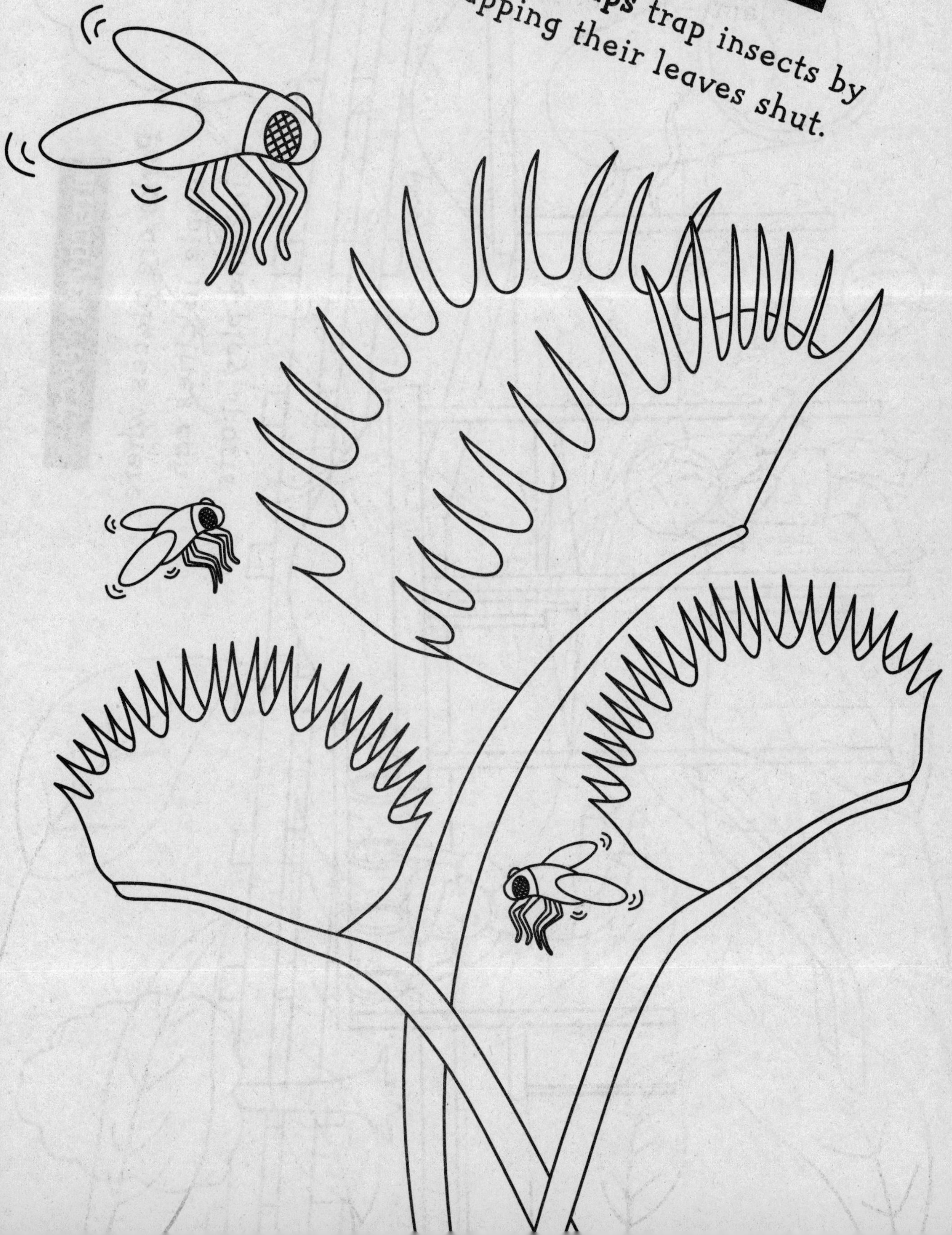

DISCOVERY FACT™

Parks are places where people in cities can relax and play sports.

Ships can dock at a **harbor** to pick up and drop off people or cargo.

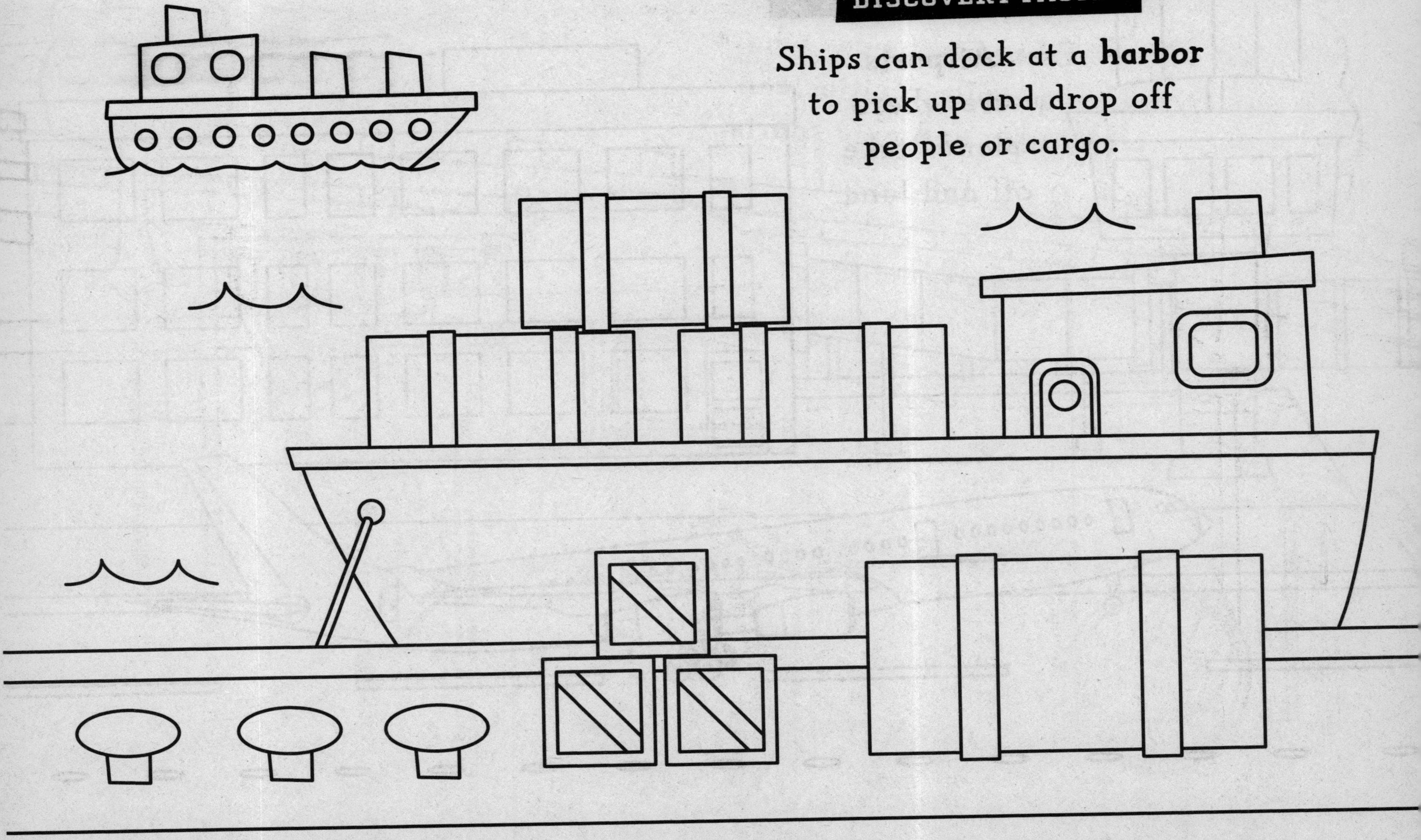

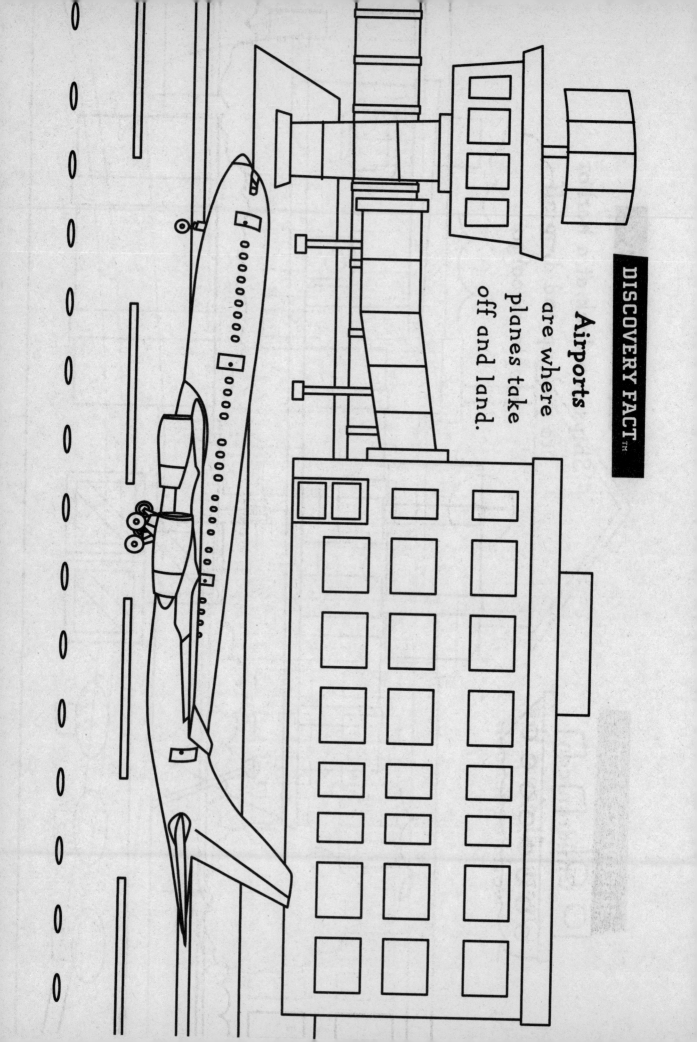

DISCOVERY FACT™

Airports are where planes take off and land.

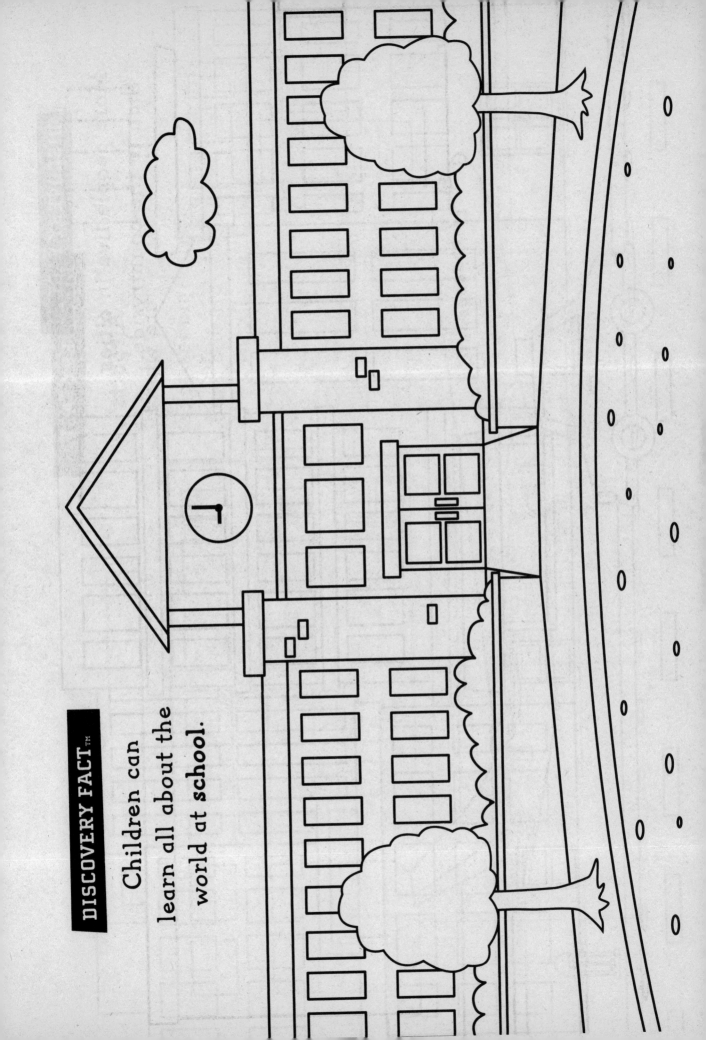

DISCOVERY FACT™

Children can learn all about the world at school.

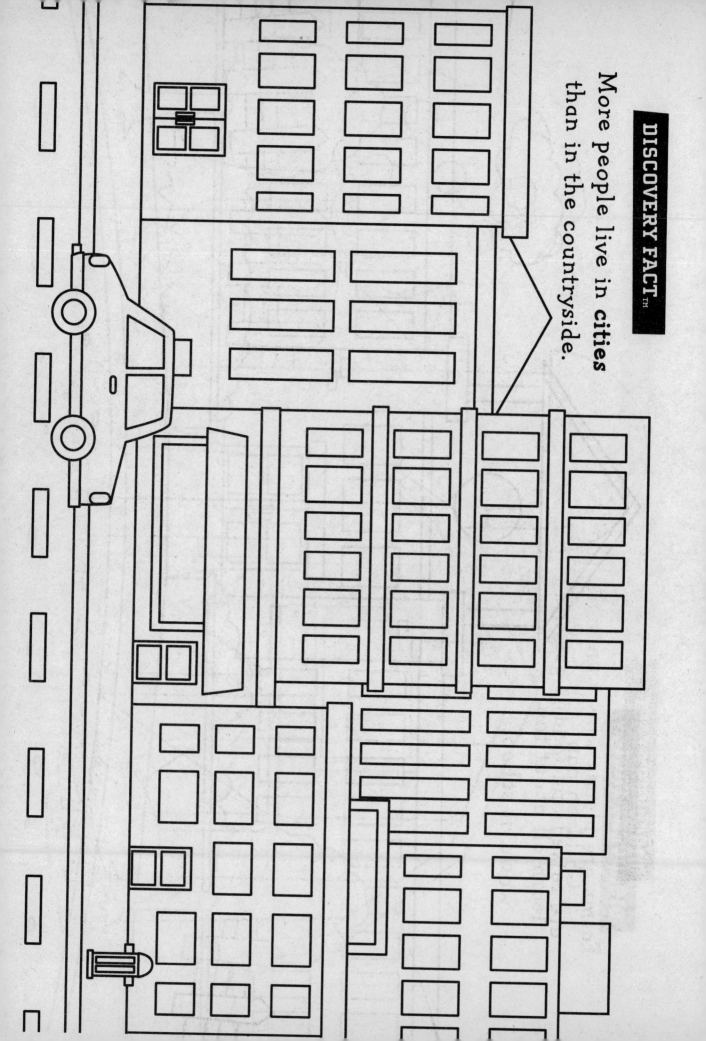

DISCOVERY FACT™

More people live in **cities** than in the countryside.

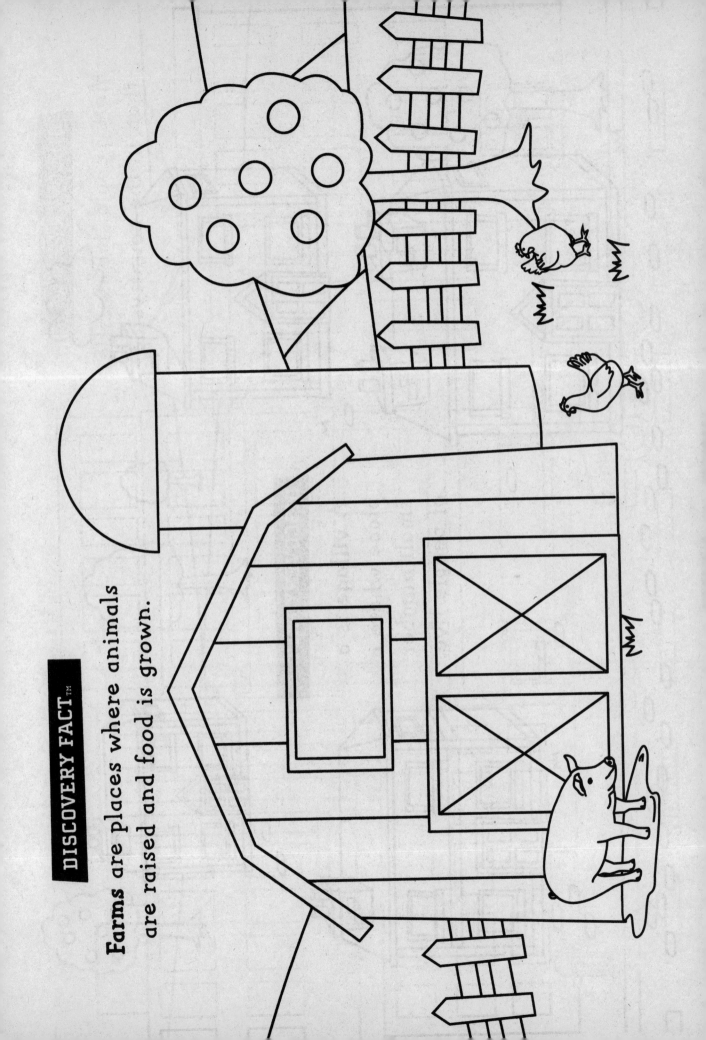

DISCOVERY FACT™

Farms are places where animals are raised and food is grown.

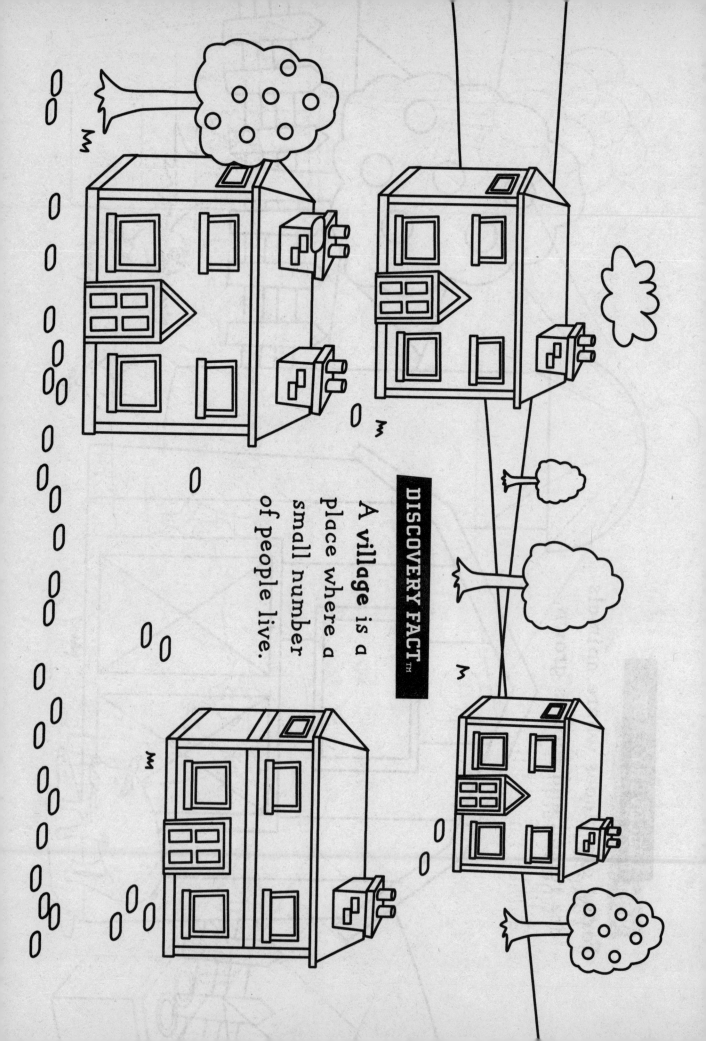

DISCOVERY FACT™

A village is a place where a small number of people live.

DISCOVERY FACT™

Fairgrounds are where people gather for a fair.

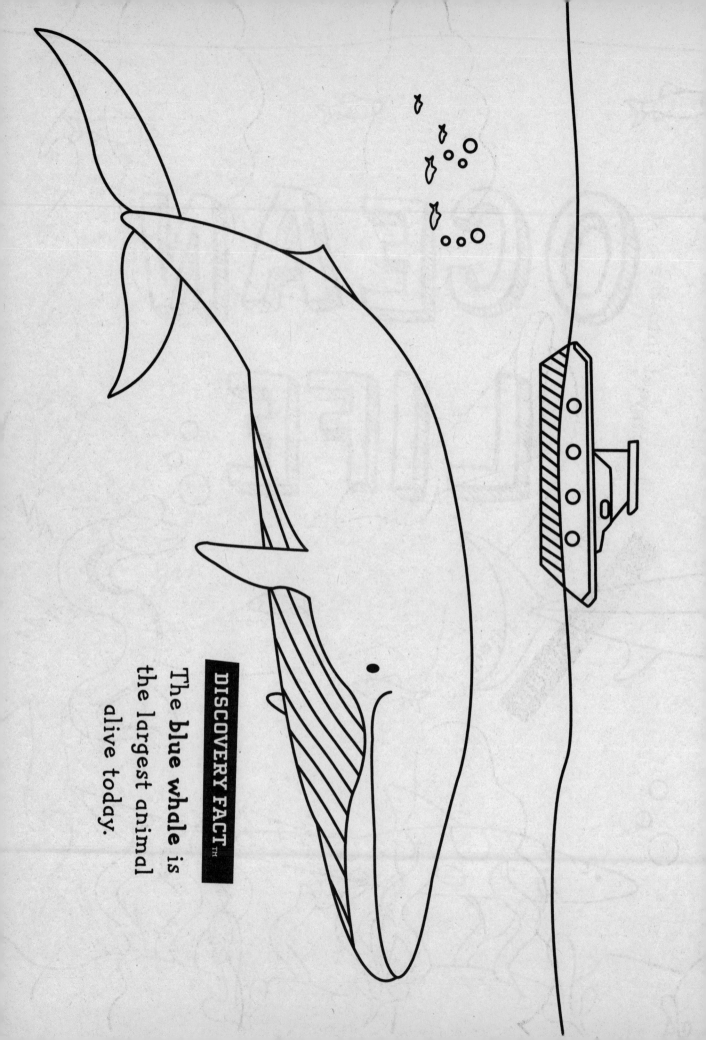

DISCOVERY FACT™

The blue whale is the largest animal alive today.

DISCOVERY FACT™

Dolphins can leap over 25 feet into the air!

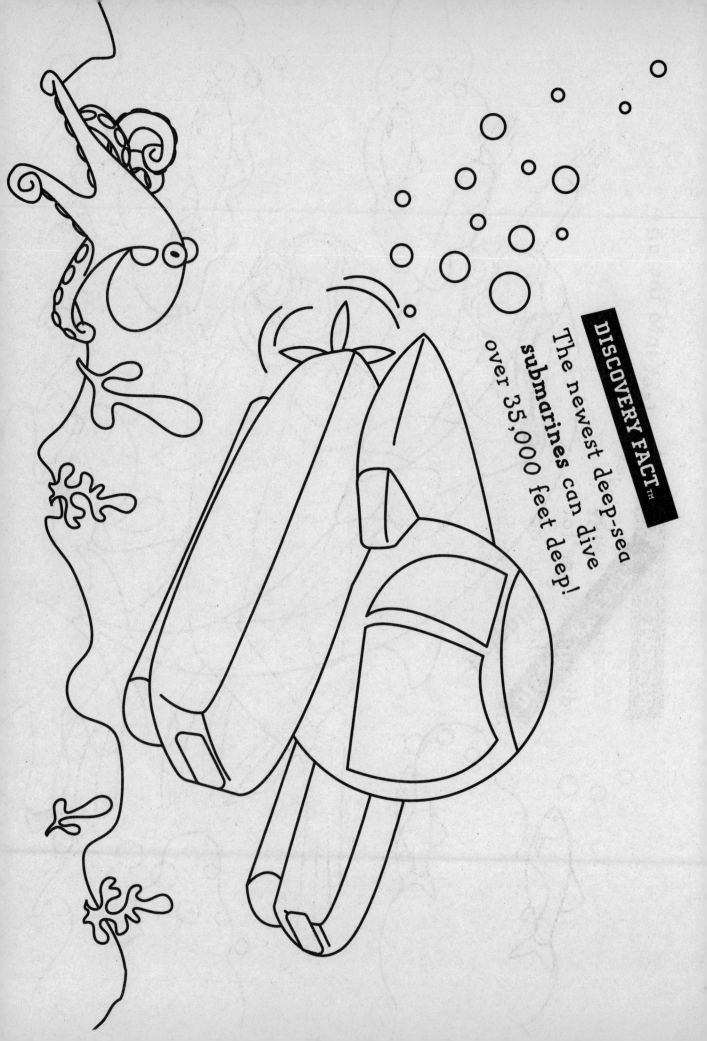

DISCOVERY FACT™

The newest deep-sea **submarines** can dive over 35,000 feet deep!

"Scuba," in scuba diving, stands for "Self-Contained Underwater Breathing Apparatus."

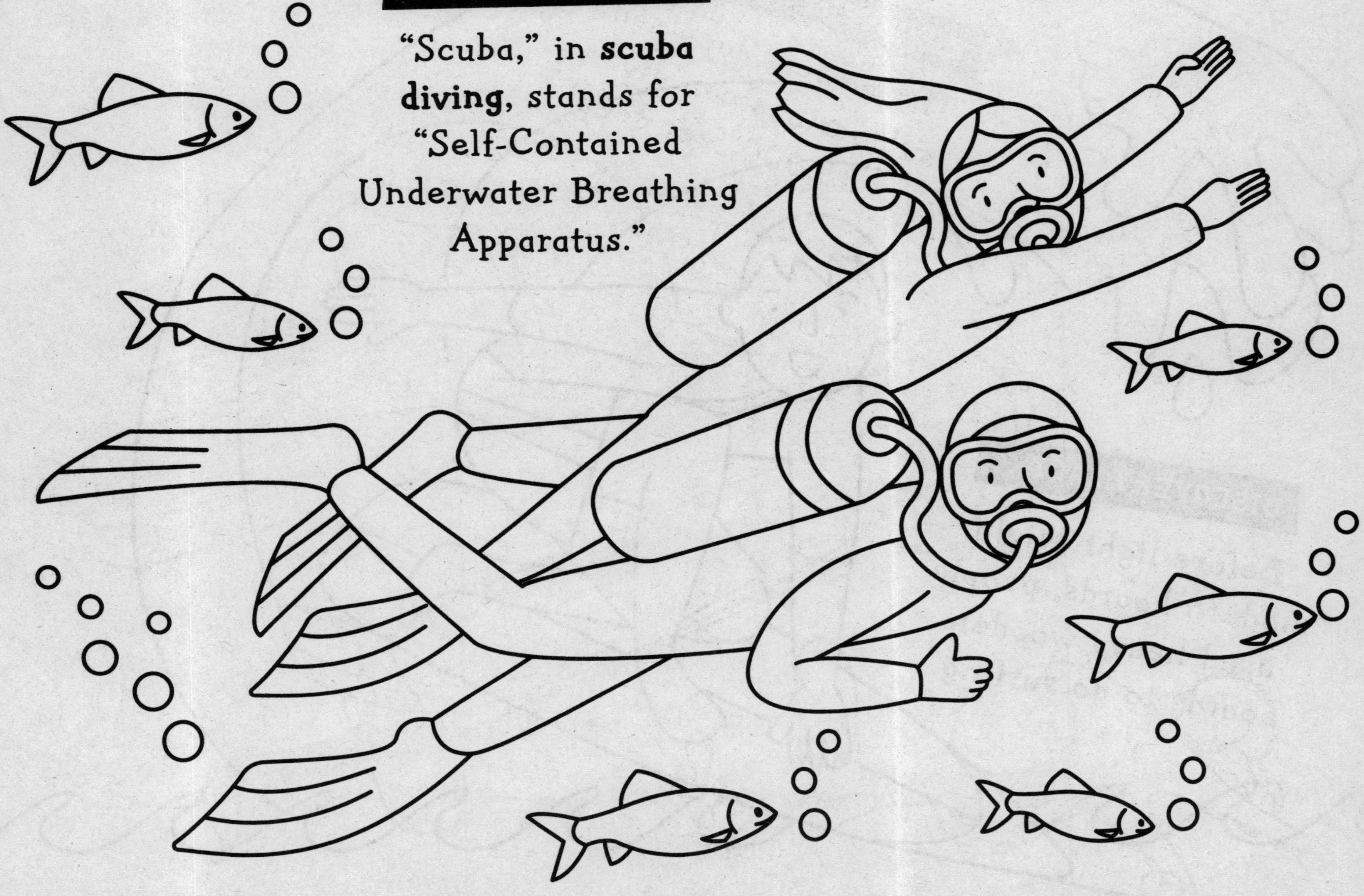

DISCOVERY FACT™

Before lightweight modern boards, people used heavy wooden boards to go **surfing**.

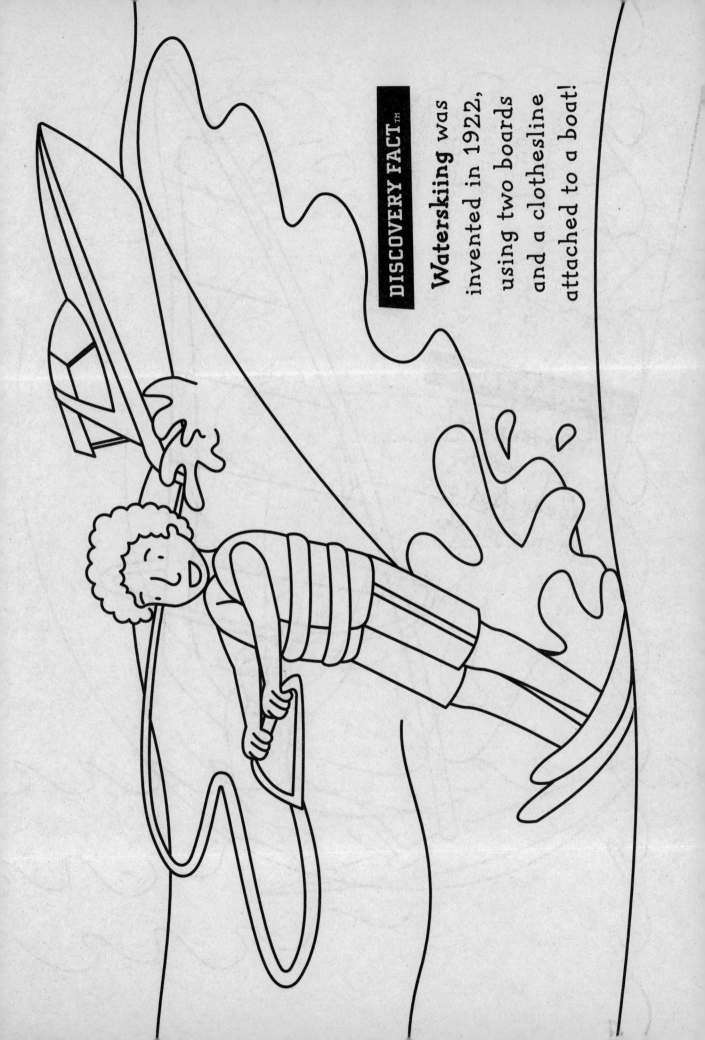

DISCOVERY FACT™

Waterskiing was invented in 1922, using two boards and a clothesline attached to a boat!

DISCOVERY FACT™

Windsurfers can reach speeds faster than a jet ski!

Some people swim underwater using a tube called a **snorkel** to breathe.

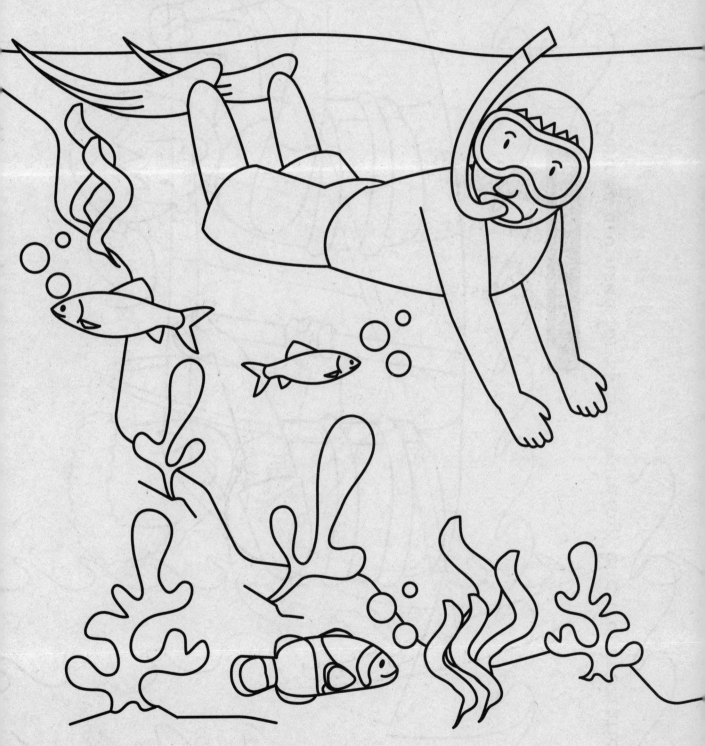

Canoes are used for sports, hunting, and transportation.

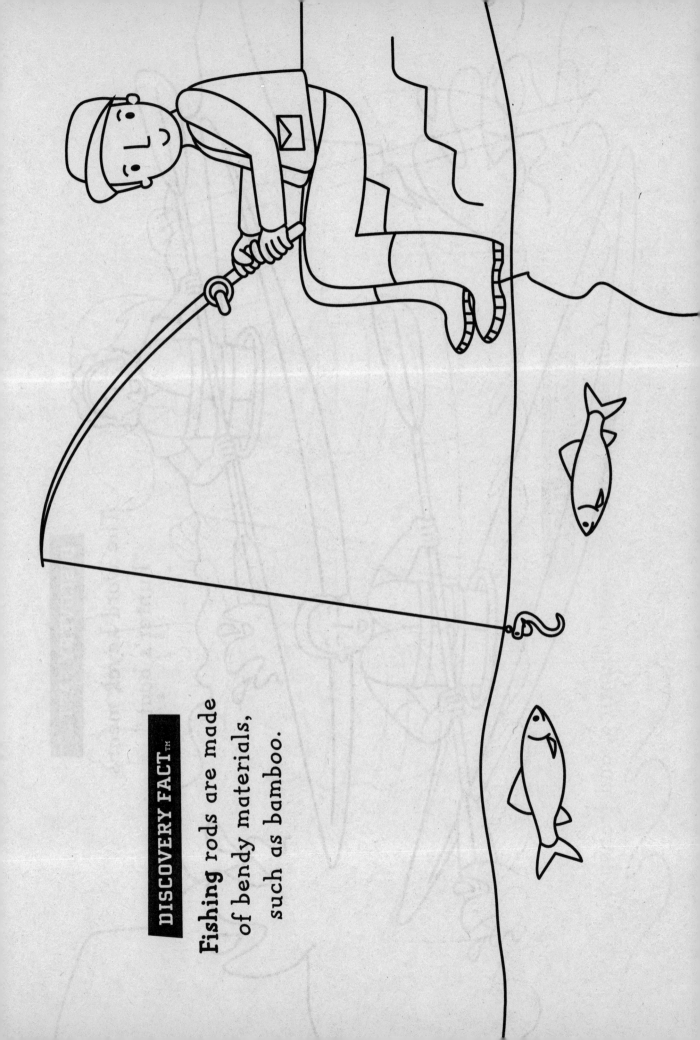

DISCOVERY FACT™

Fishing rods are made of bendy materials, such as bamboo.

DISCOVERY FACT™

The word *kayak* means
"hunter's boat."

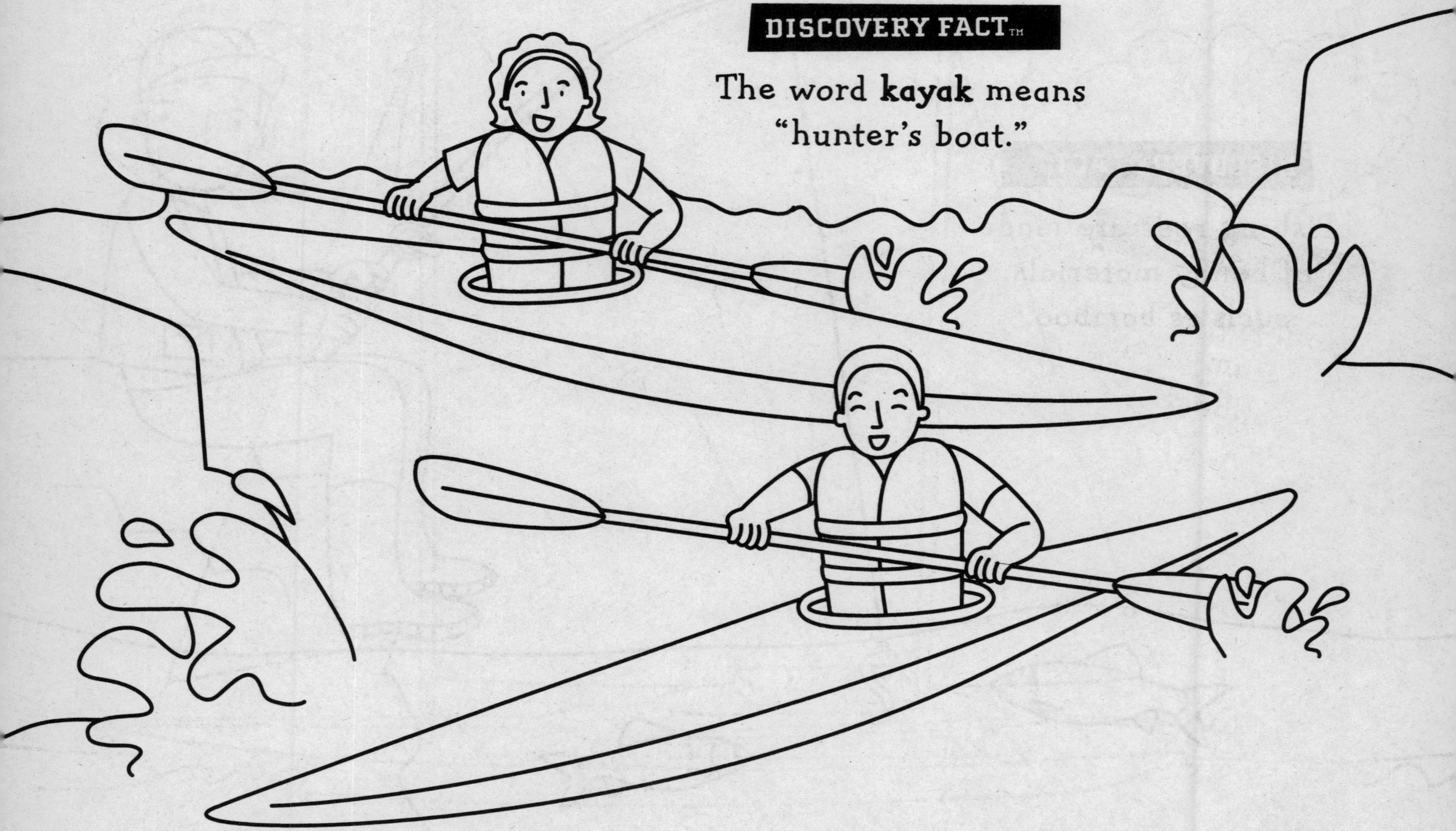

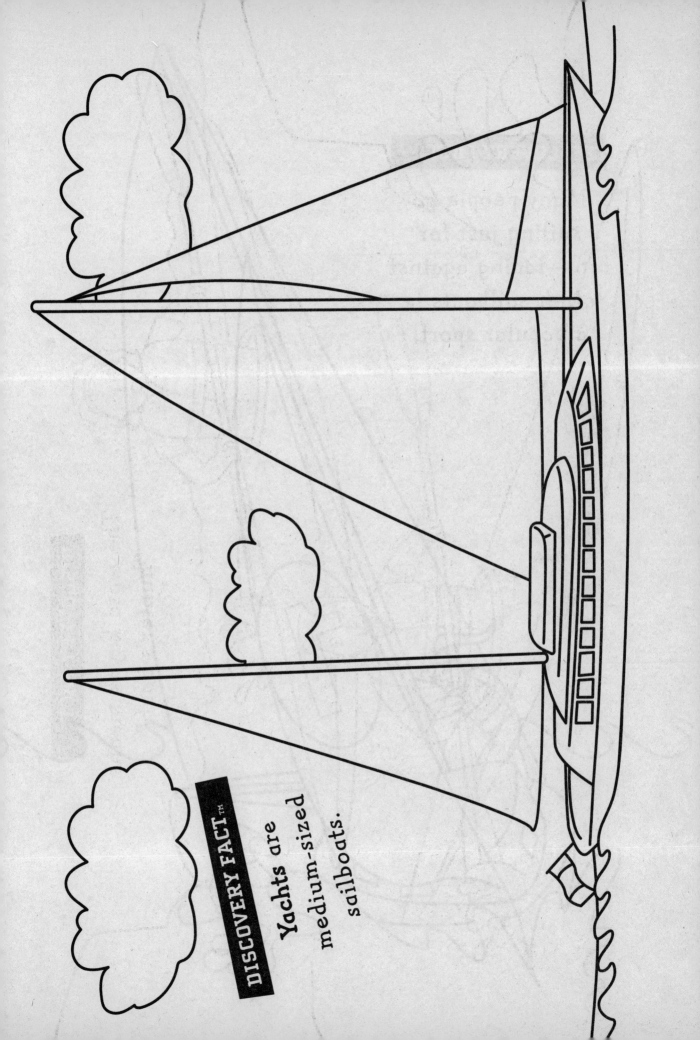

DISCOVERY FACT™

Yachts are medium-sized sailboats.

Many people go **sailing** just for fun—racing against other sailboats is a popular sport!

DISCOVERY FACT™

Kite surfing is like surfing, kite flying, and wakeboarding all at once!

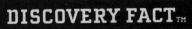

DISCOVERY FACT™

The **electric eel** can scare off hunters with a nasty electric shock!

DISCOVERY FACT™

Marine angelfish are famous for their super-bright colors.

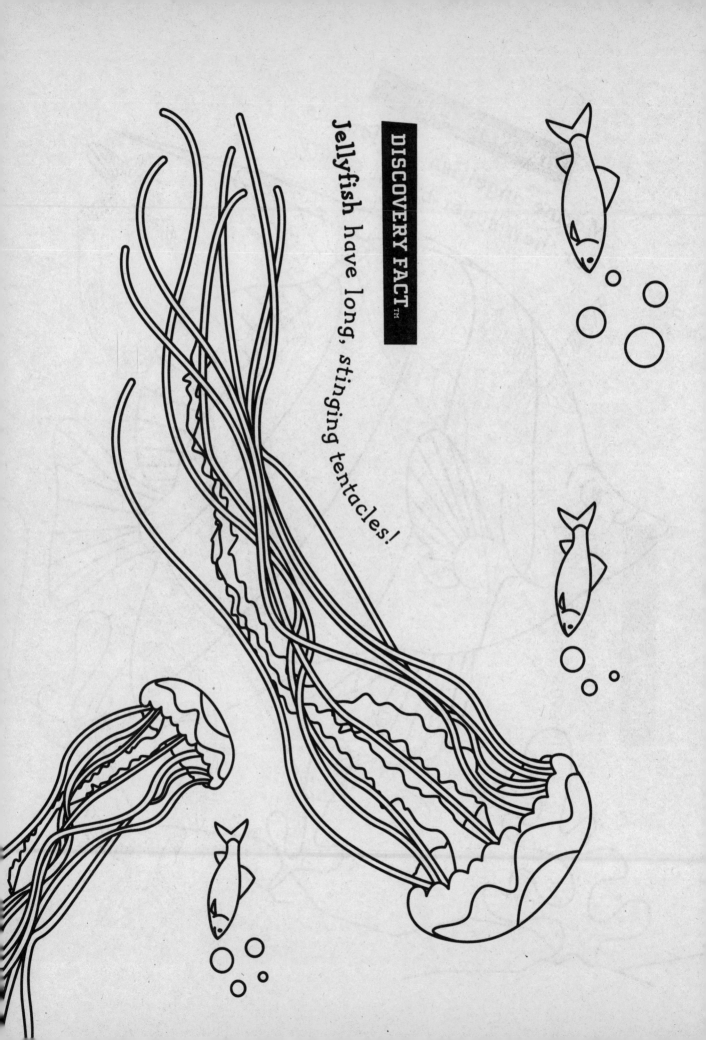

DISCOVERY FACT™

Jellyfish have long, stinging tentacles!

The name piranha means "fish tooth"!

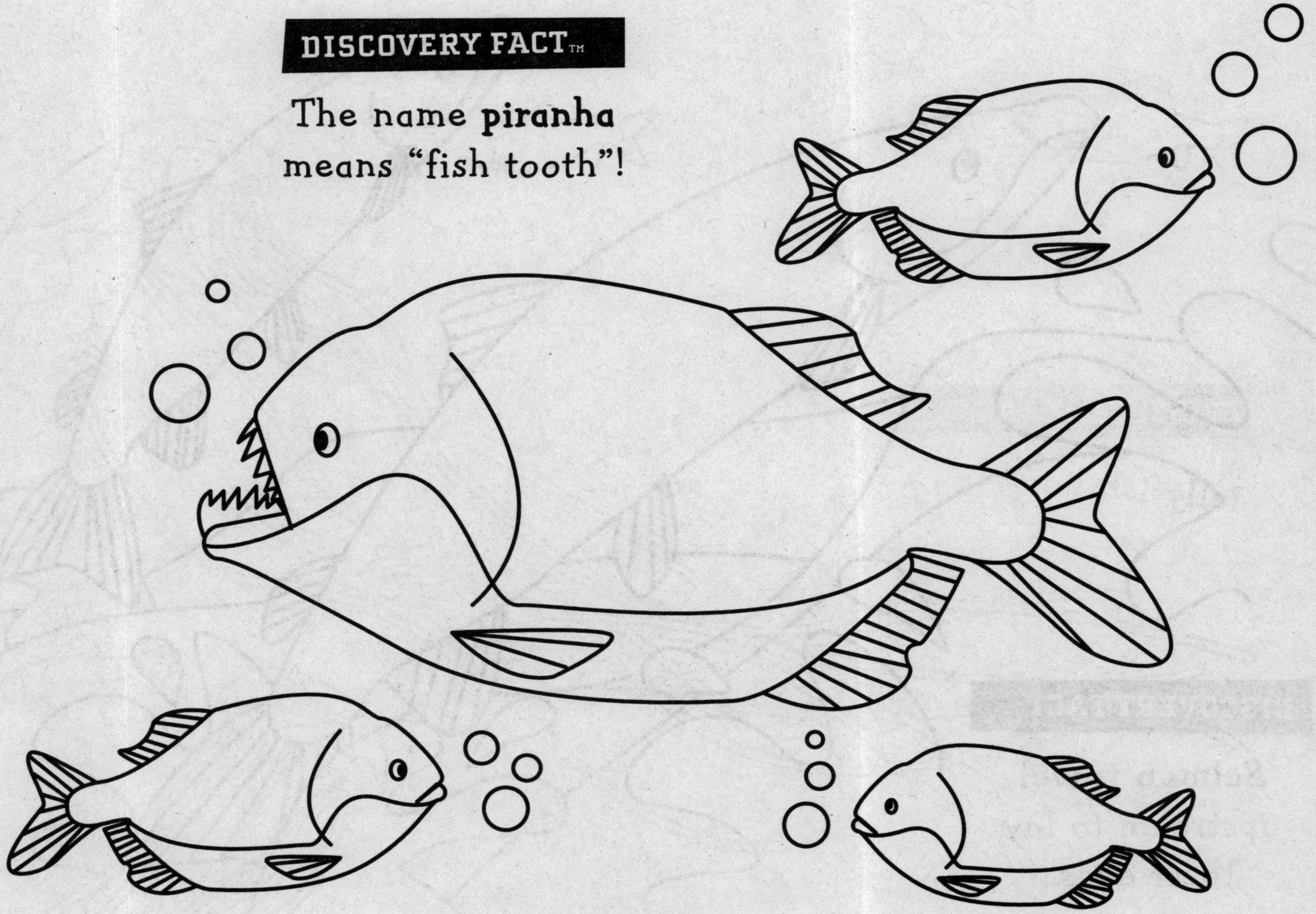

DISCOVERY FACT ™

Salmon travel upstream to lay their eggs.

DISCOVERY FACT™

Tuna can reach speeds of up to 40 miles per hour—that's as fast as a car!

DISCOVERY FACT™

If an **octopus**
loses a tentacle,
it can grow
another one!

DISCOVERY FACT ™

Manta rays can weigh up to 2 tons, but they can still leap from the water!

DISCOVERY FACT™

Swordfish snouts have long, pointed that look like a sword!

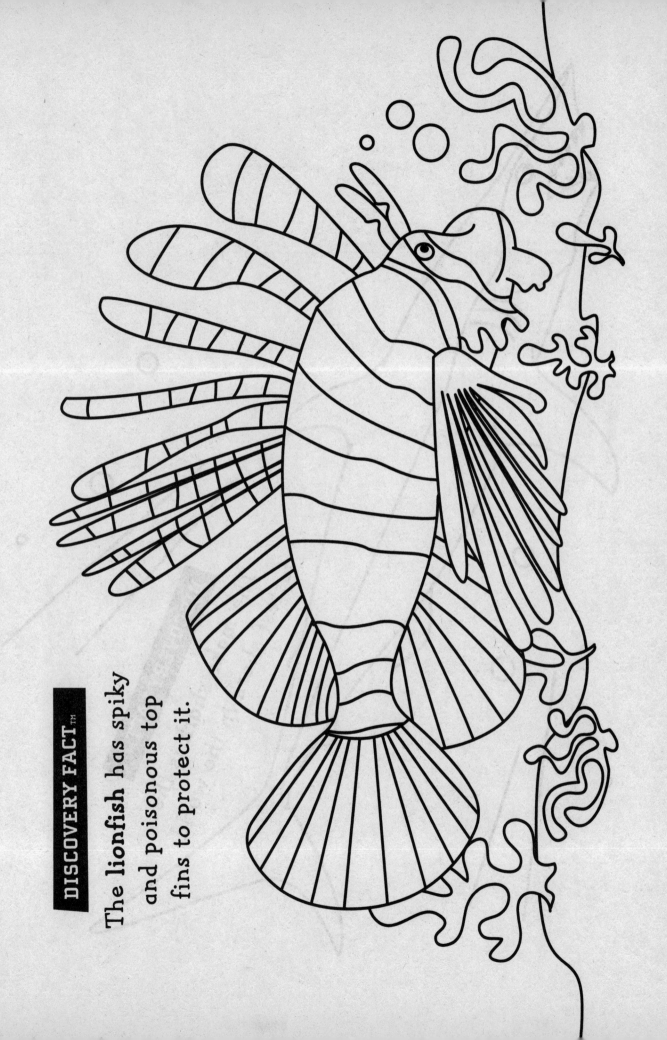

DISCOVERY FACT™

The lionfish has spiky and poisonous top fins to protect it.

DISCOVERY FACT™

The mako shark is the fastest shark in the world.

A **seahorse** uses its tail to grasp objects, and as an anchor.

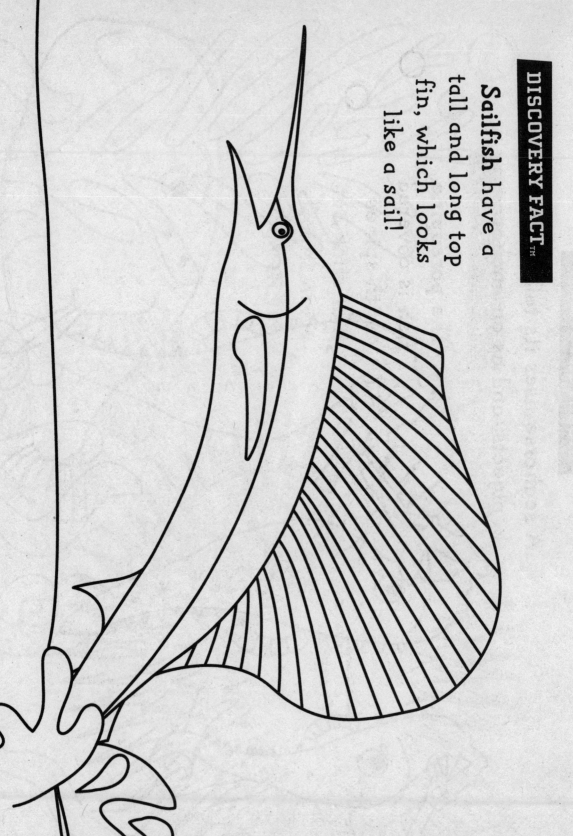

Sailfish have a
tall and long top
fin, which looks
like a sail!

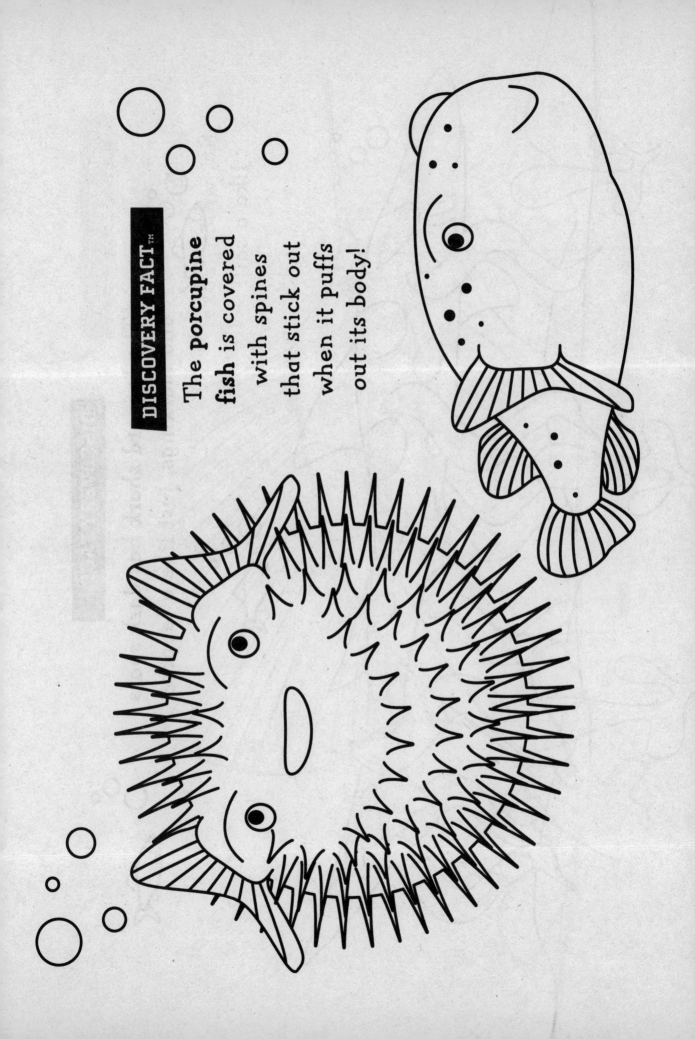

The porcupine fish is covered with spines that stick out when it puffs out its body!

DISCOVERY FACT ™

The leopard shark has dark spots
and markings, just like a leopard.

Blacktip reef sharks have a striking black tip on their fins.

DISCOVERY FACT™

Wobbegongs are patterned, flat sharks that can easily hide against the sea floor.

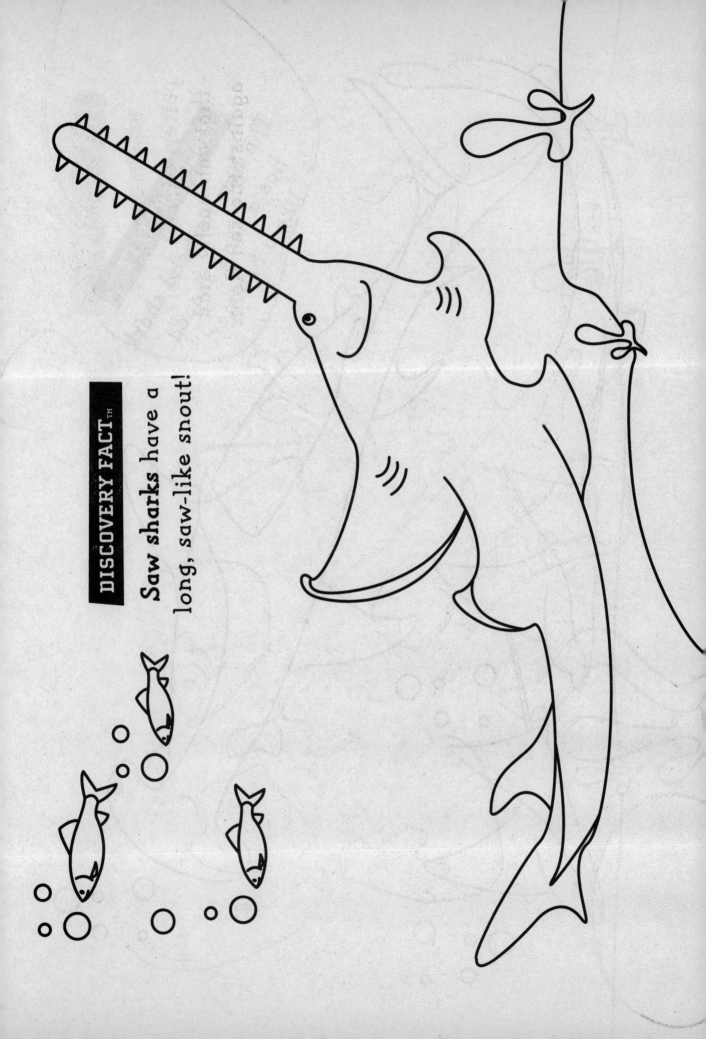

DISCOVERY FACT™

Saw sharks have a long, saw-like snout!

DISCOVERY FACT™

The hammerhead shark has a head shaped like a hammer!

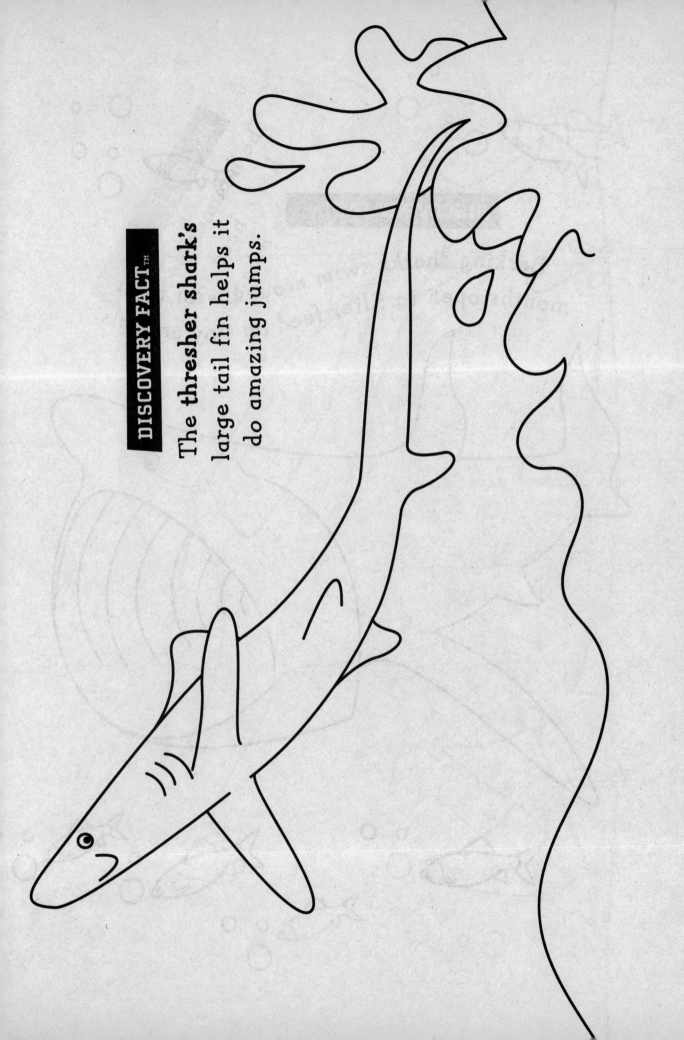

DISCOVERY FACT™

The thresher shark's large tail fin helps it do amazing jumps.

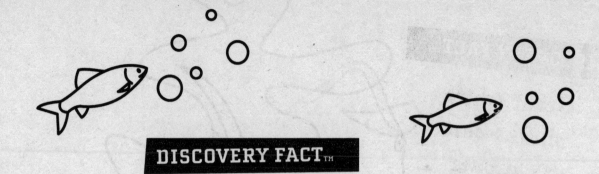

DISCOVERY FACT™

Basking sharks swim around with their mouths open to filter feed on tiny animals.

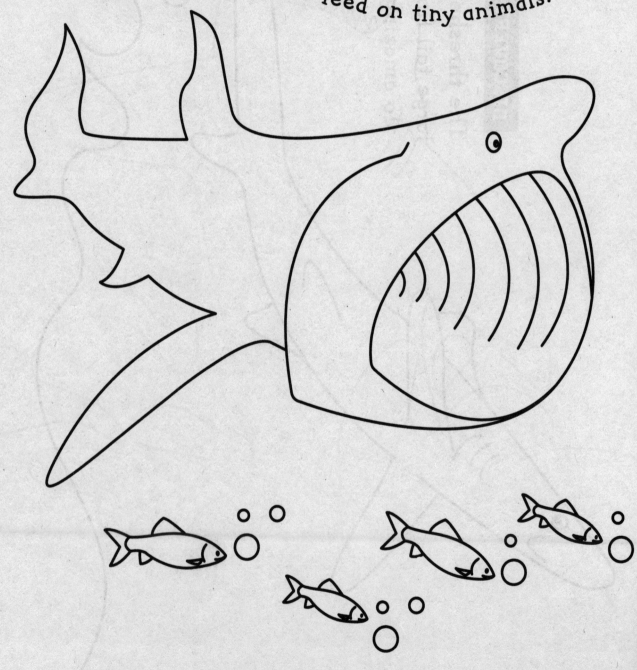

Great white
sharks can
have over
300 teeth!

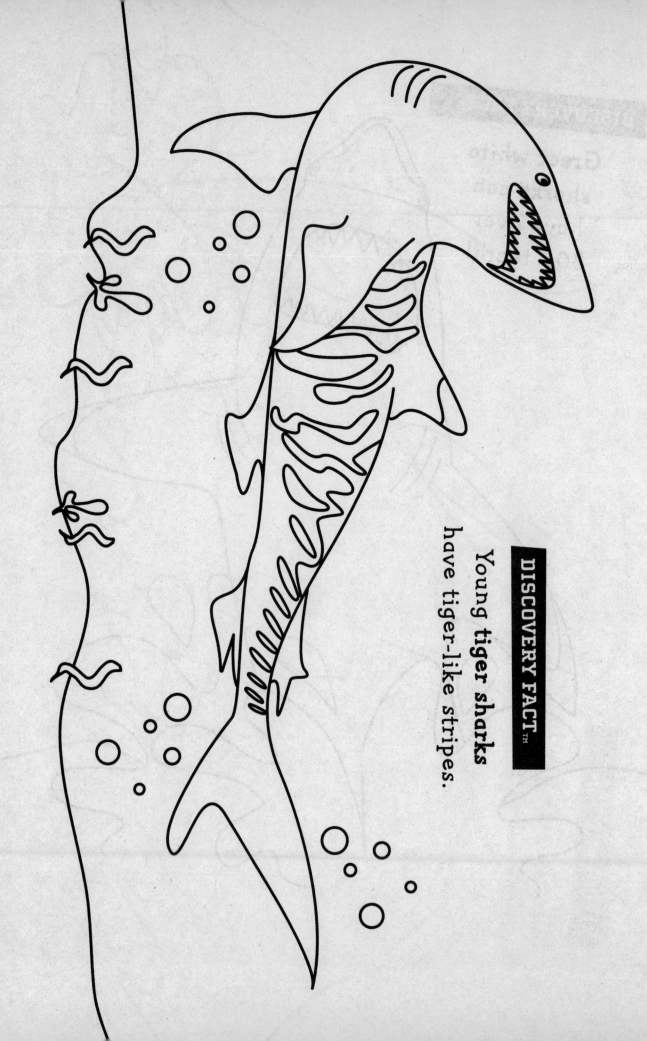

DISCOVERY FACT™

Young tiger sharks have tiger-like stripes.

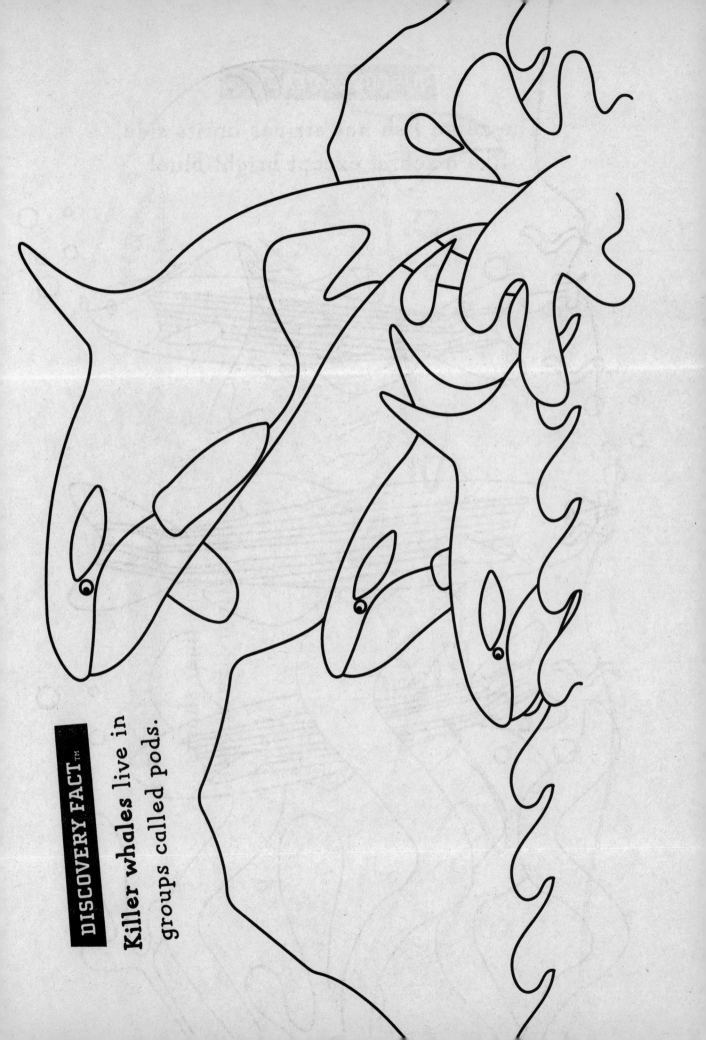

DISCOVERY FACT™

Killer whales live in groups called pods.

The **zebra fish** has stripes on its side,
like a zebra, except bright blue!

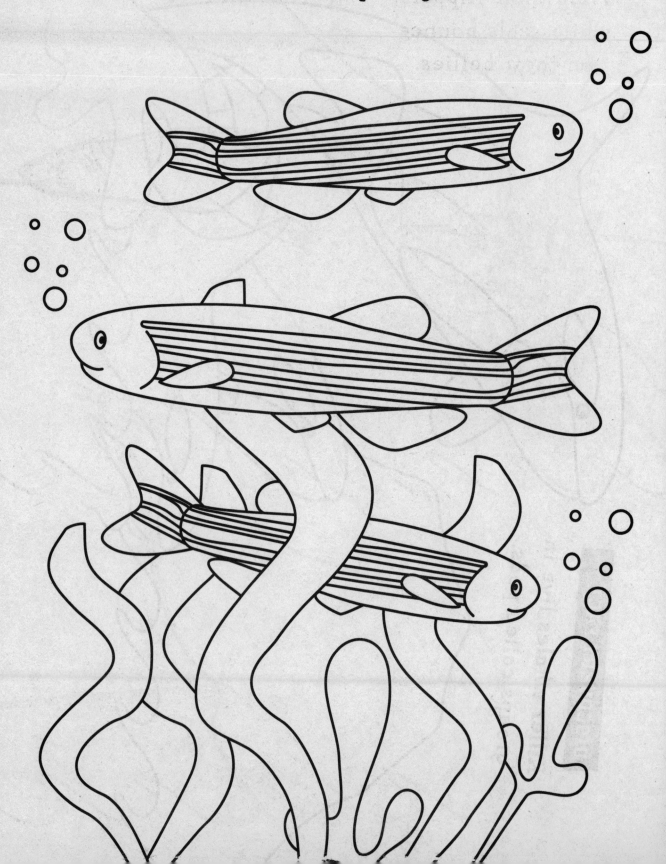

Sea lions walk using their flippers, while seals bounce on their bellies.

DISCOVERY FACT™

Porpoises are smaller and have a shorter beak than dolphins.

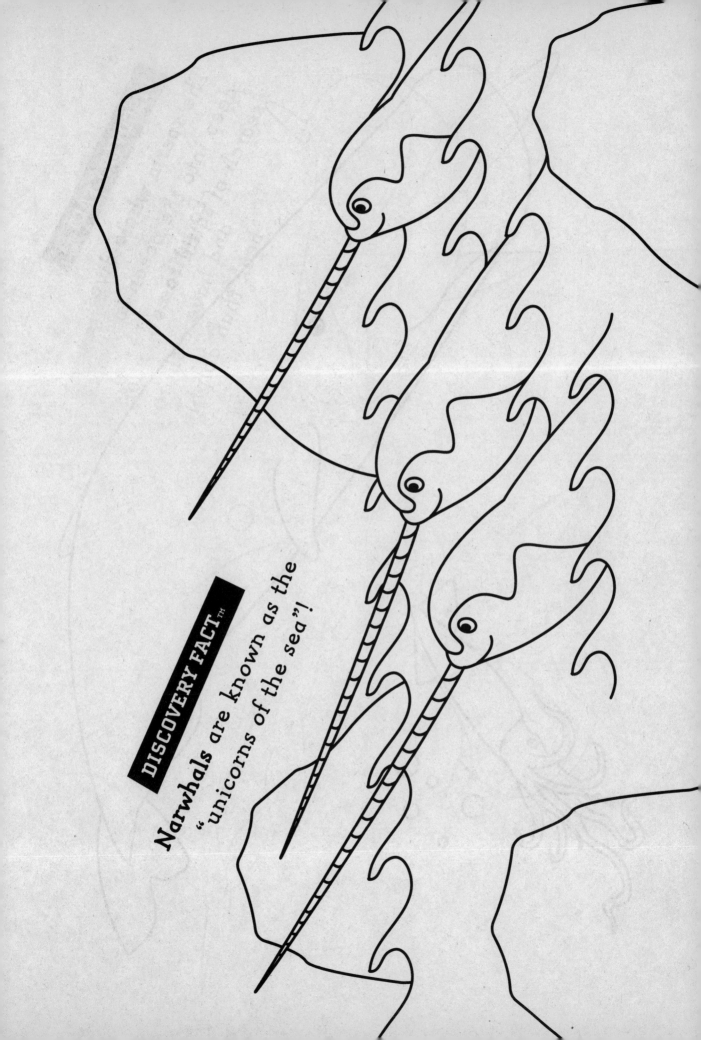

DISCOVERY FACT™

Narwhals are known as the "unicorns of the sea"!

DISCOVERY FACT™

The **sperm whale** dives deep into the ocean in search of squid to eat!

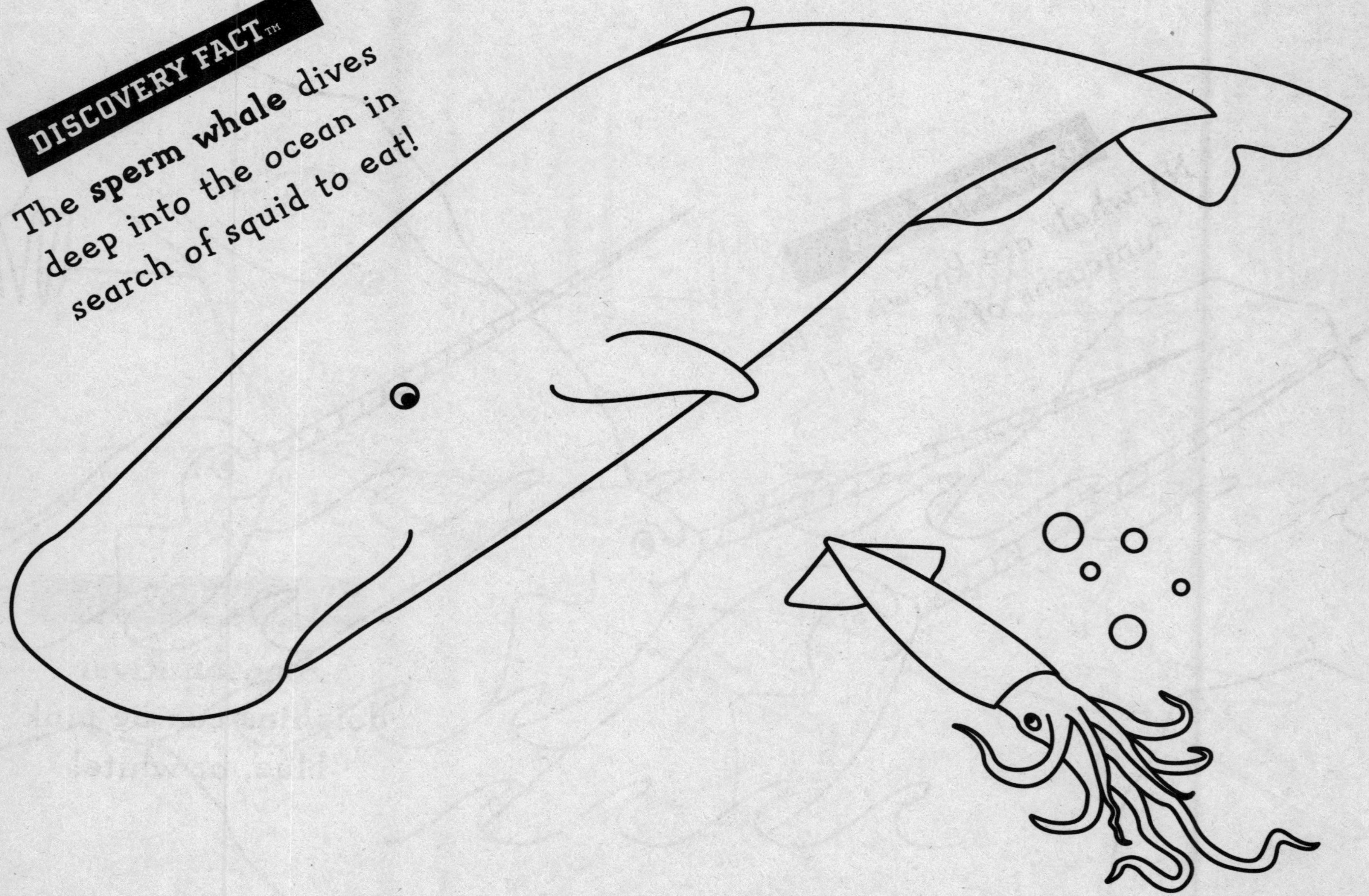

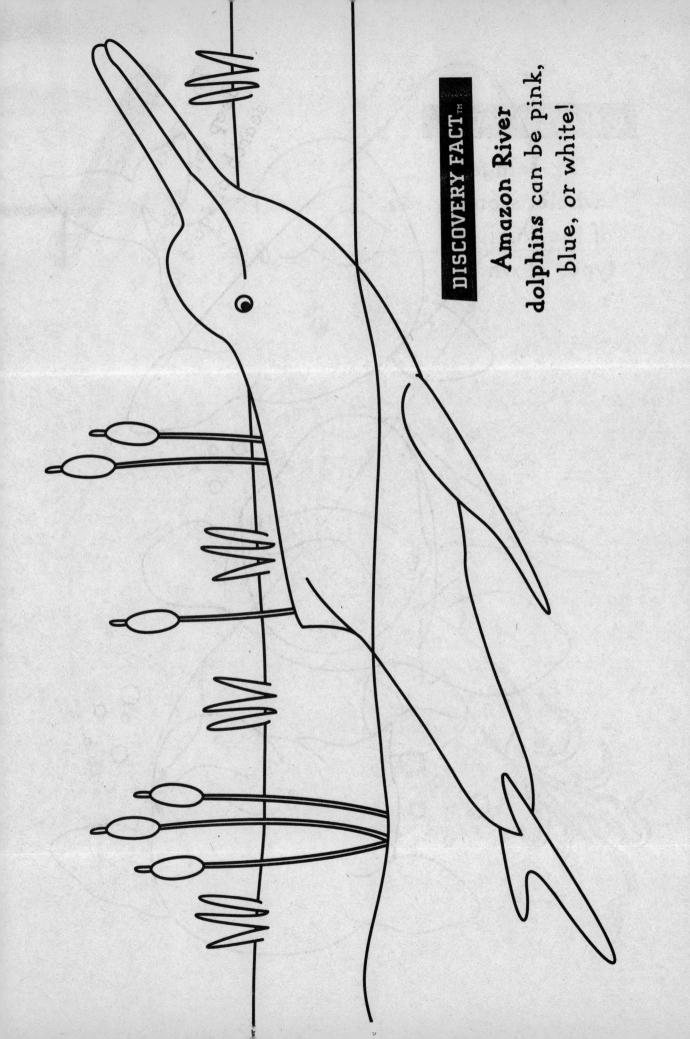

DISCOVERY FACT™

Amazon River dolphins can be pink, blue, or white!

The **beluga whale** is one of the smallest types of whale.

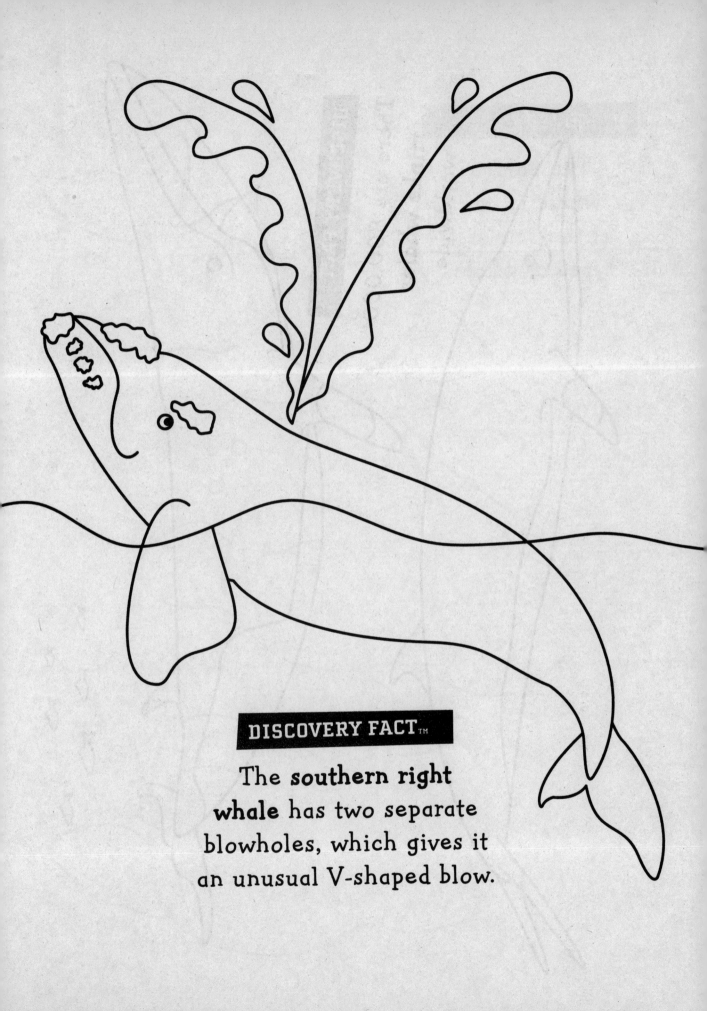

DISCOVERY FACT™

The **southern right whale** has two separate blowholes, which gives it an unusual V-shaped blow.

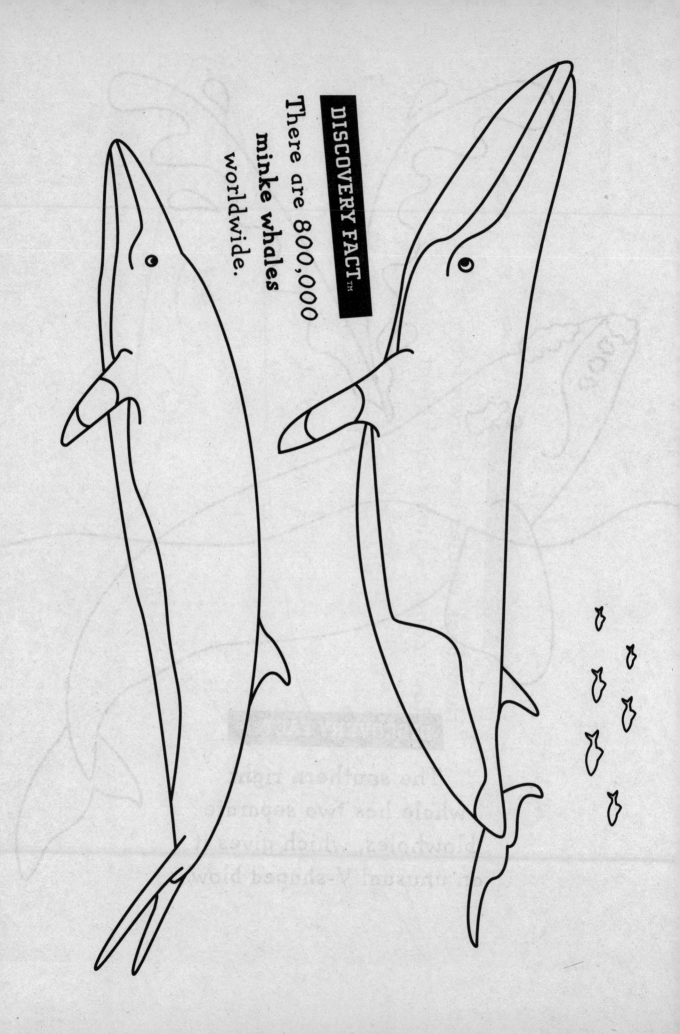

DISCOVERY FACT™

There are 800,000 minke whales worldwide.

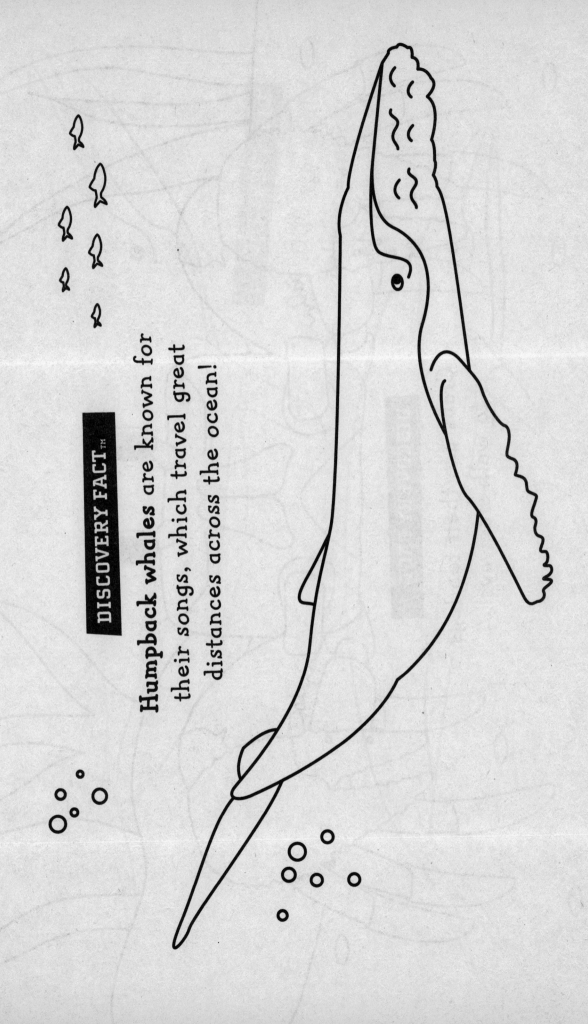

DISCOVERY FACT™

Humpback whales are known for their songs, which travel great distances across the ocean!

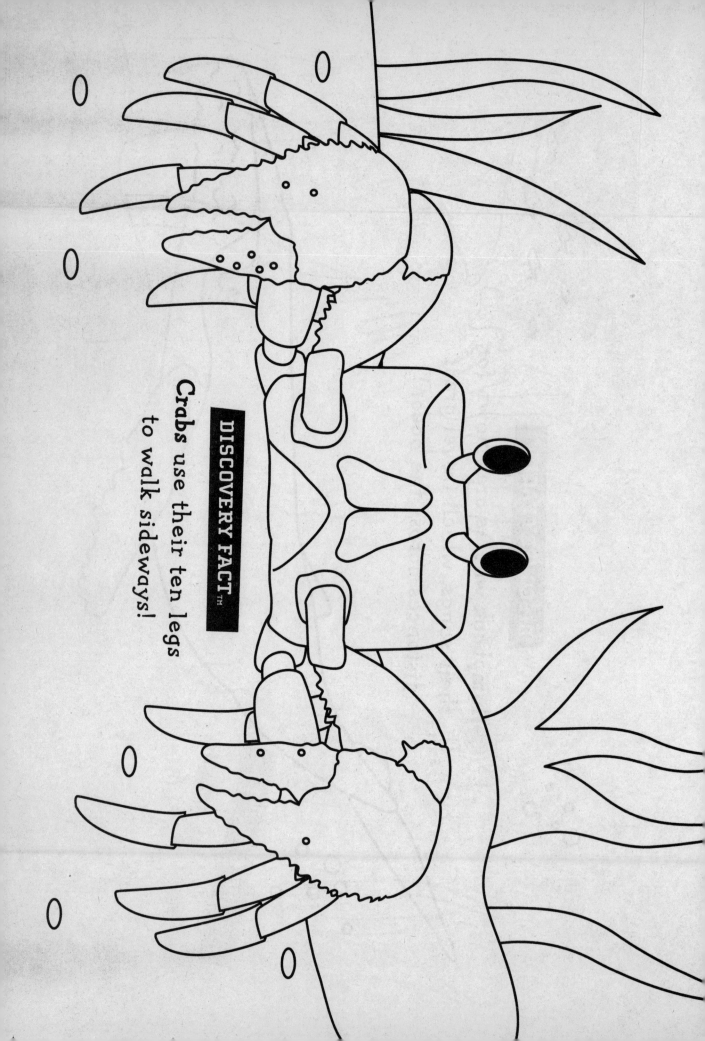

DISCOVERY FACT™

Crabs use their ten legs
to walk sideways!

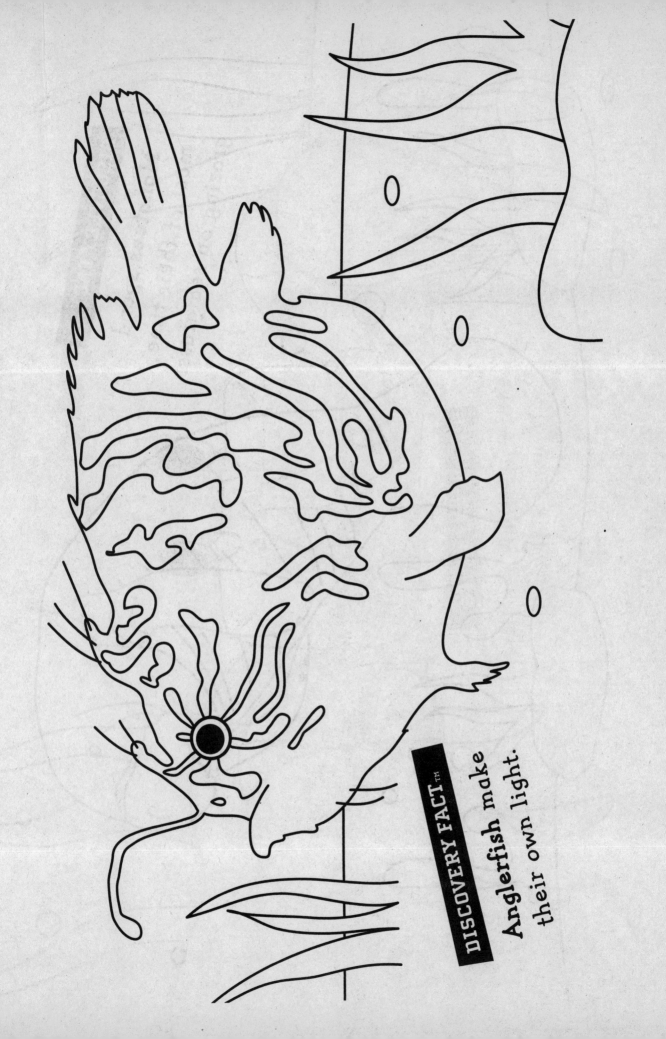

DISCOVERY FACT™

Anglerfish make their own light.

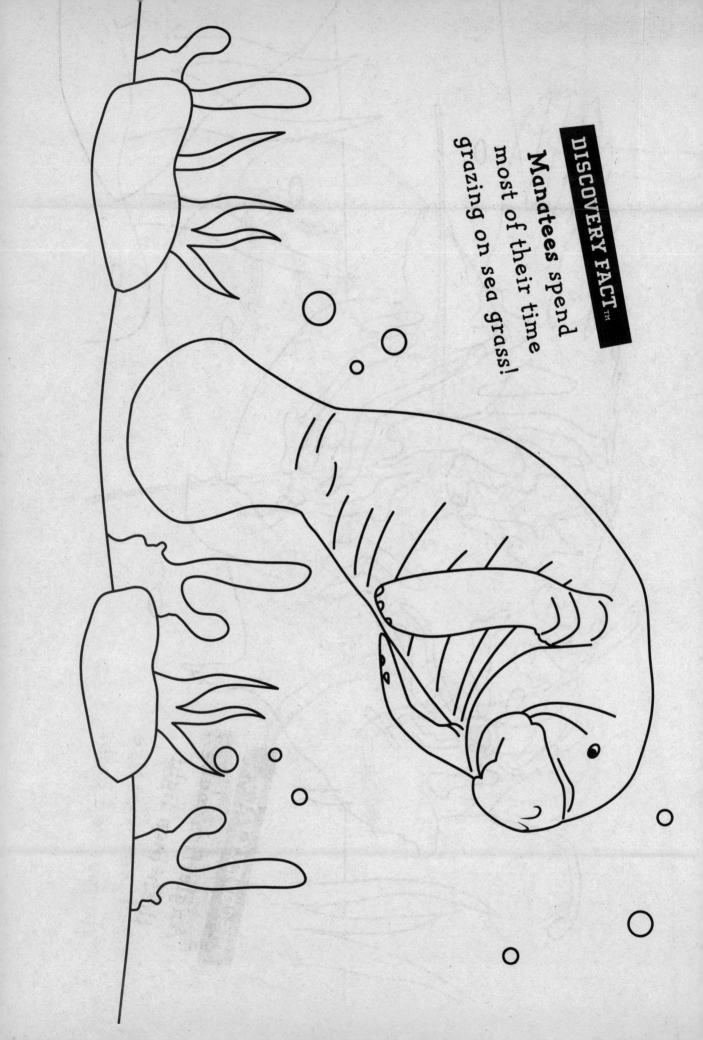

DISCOVERY FACT™

Manatees spend
most of their time
grazing on sea grass!

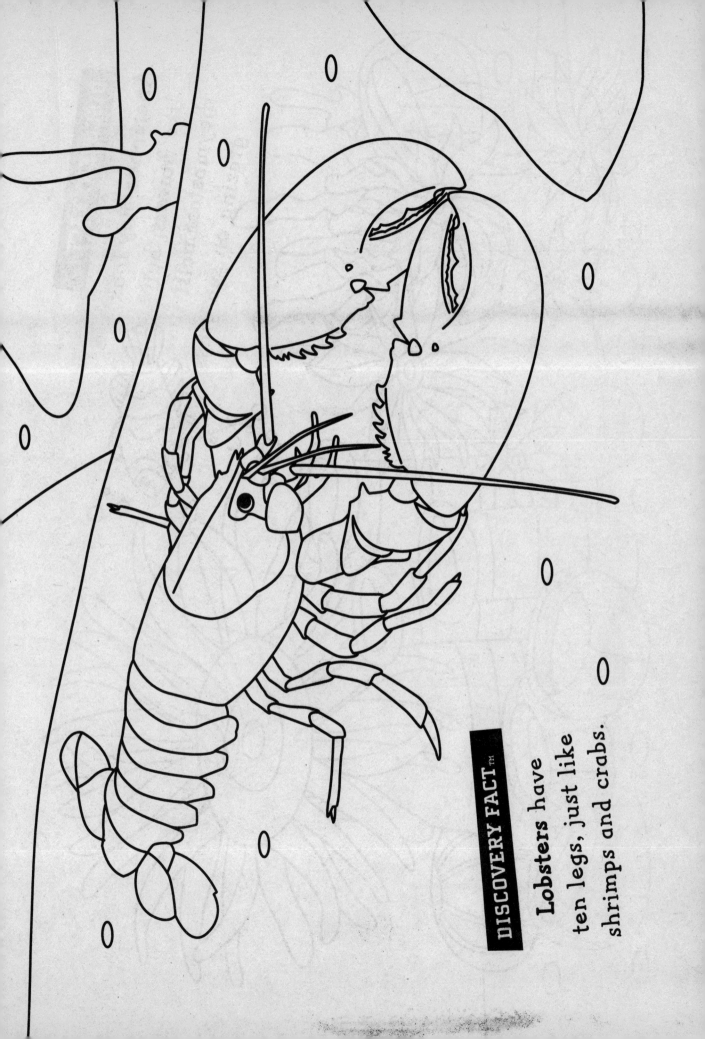

DISCOVERY FACT™

Lobsters have ten legs, just like shrimps and crabs.

DISCOVERY FACT™

Anemones may look like flowers, but they are animals!

Giant squids have the largest eyes of any animal in the world.

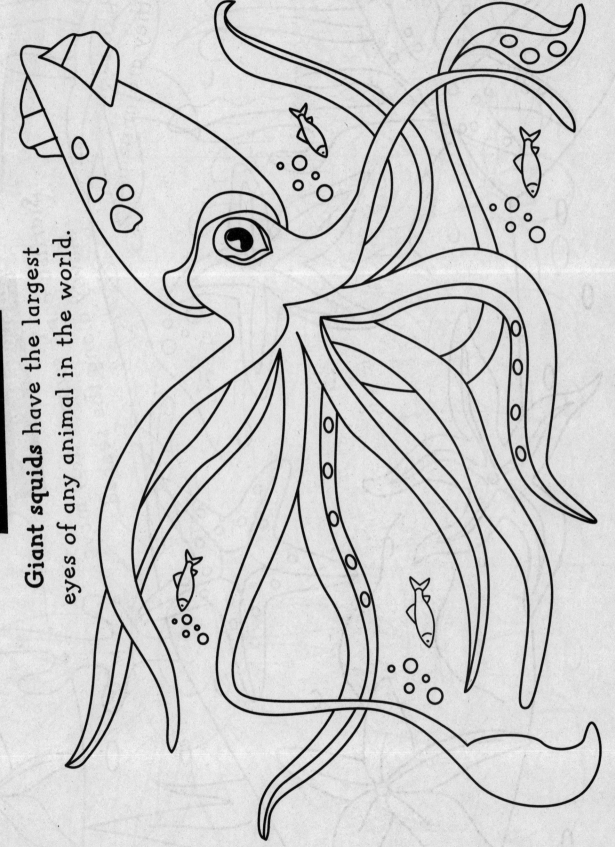

DISCOVERY FACT™

Starfish can't swim—they move slowly along the seabed.

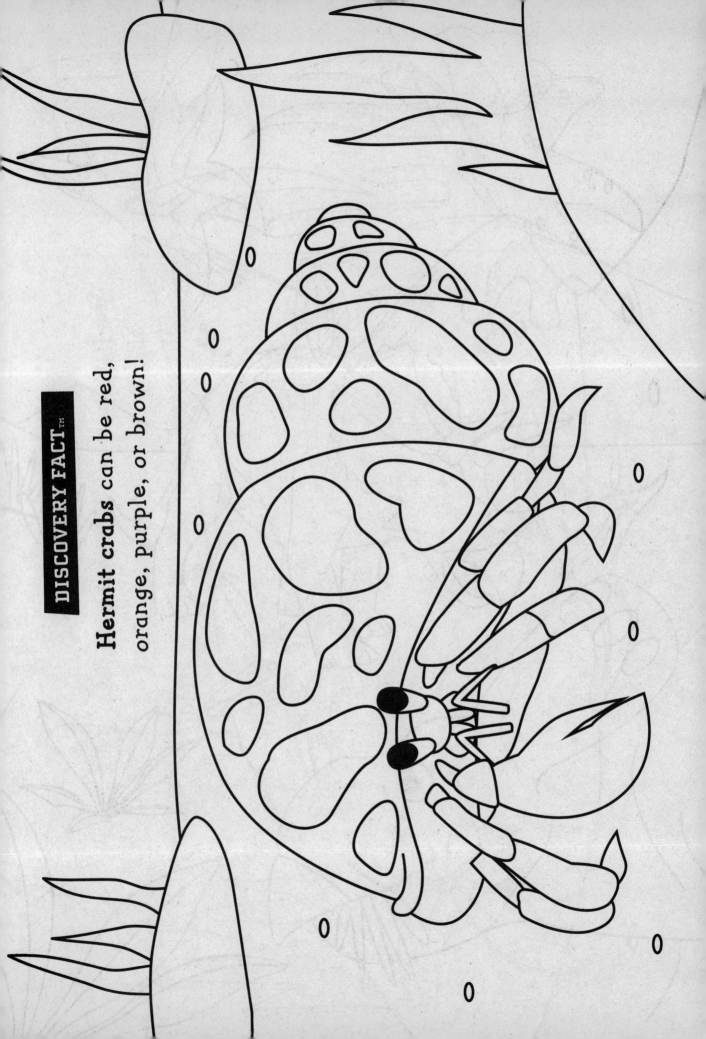

DISCOVERY FACT™

Hermit crabs can be red, orange, purple, or brown!

ANIMALS FROM THE PAST

DISCOVERY FACT™

Coelophysis
which made it a light and fast hunter!
had hollow bones,

DISCOVERY FACT™

Plateosaurus had five-fingered hands and a large thumb claw!

DISCOVERY FACT ™

The plant-eating **Heterodontosaurus** had three kinds of teeth for chomping and chewing!

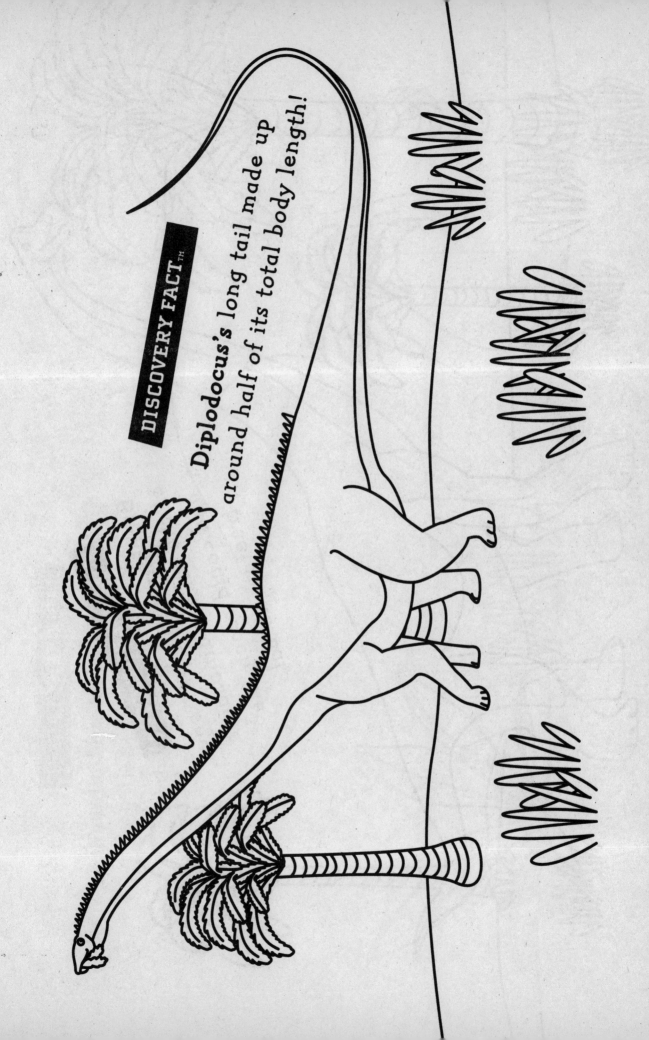

DISCOVERY FACT™

Diplodocus's long tail made up around half of its total body length!

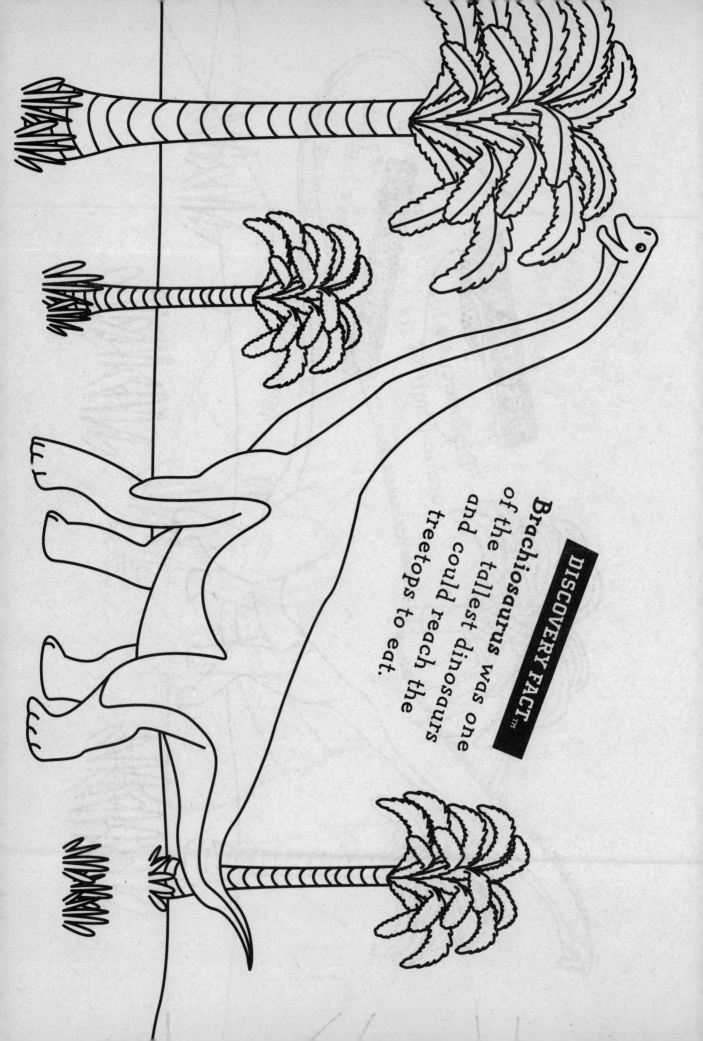

DISCOVERY FACT ™

Brachiosaurus was one of the tallest dinosaurs and could reach the treetops to eat.

DISCOVERY FACT™

Tyrannosaurus rex had a powerful, bone-crushing bite!

Spinosaurus had a huge sail on its back that grew over 5 feet high!

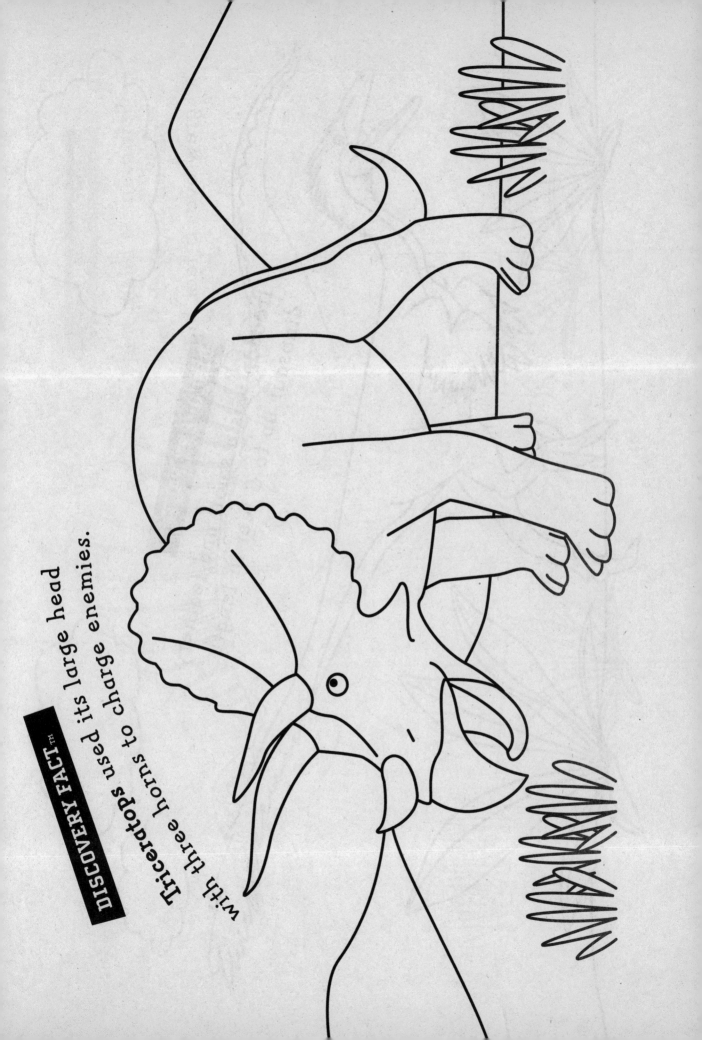

DISCOVERY FACT™

Triceratops used its large head with three horns to charge enemies.

DISCOVERY FACT™

Troodon was a small and feathery dinosaur up to 8 feet in length.

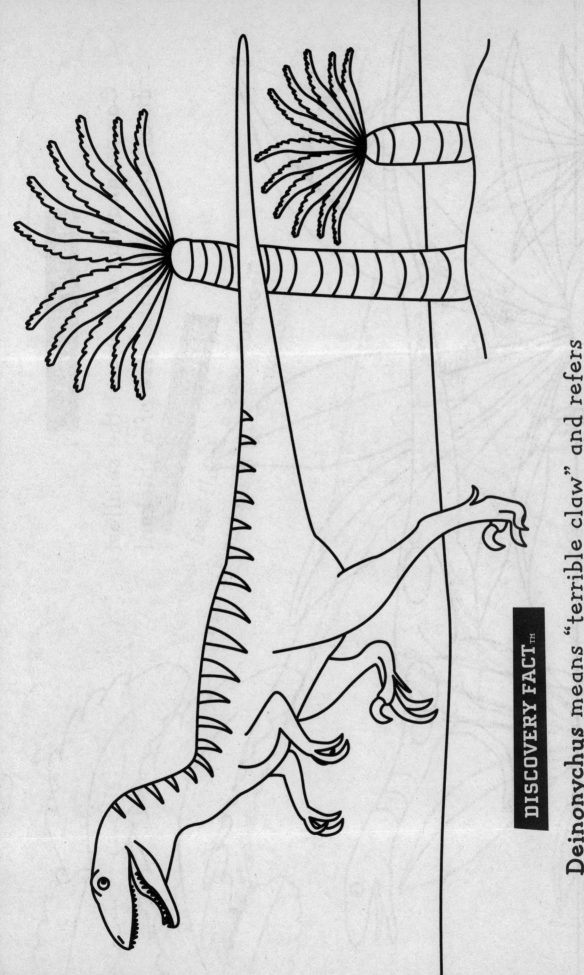

DISCOVERY FACT™

Deinonychus means "terrible claw" and refers to the hooked claws on its hind feet!

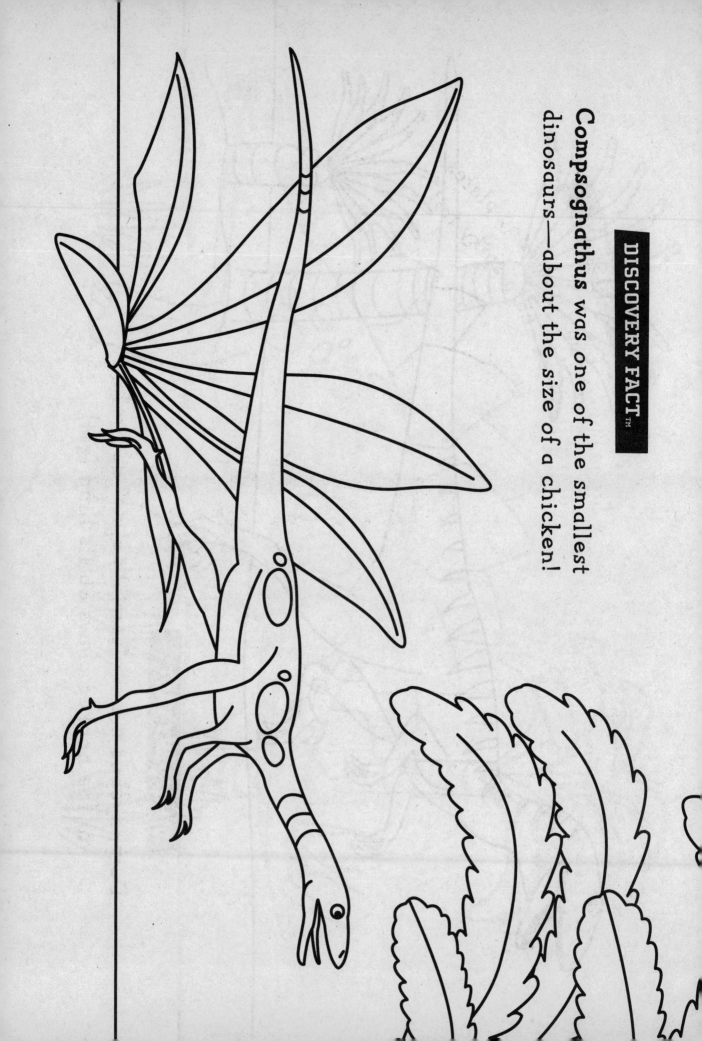

DISCOVERY FACT™

Compsognathus was one of the smallest dinosaurs—about the size of a chicken!

DISCOVERY FACT™

Stegosaurus had large bony plates along its back and a spiky tail.

DISCOVERY FACT™

Struthiomimus looked like a featherless ostrich and was a super-fast runner.

DISCOVERY FACT™

Hypsilophodon was one of the few dinosaurs that had cheeks! It stored food in them while it chewed.

Euoplocephalus had a hammer
at the end of its tail!

DISCOVERY FACT™

Kentrosaurus grew up to 17 feet long, but this big dinosaur had a brain the size of a walnut!

DISCOVERY FACT™

Protoceratops had a sharp parrot-like beak and a jaw packed with dozens of teeth.

Polacanthus had body armor to protect itself, including sharp spikes from neck to tail.

Parasaurolophus had a hollow head crest, which it used to make sounds like a trumpet.

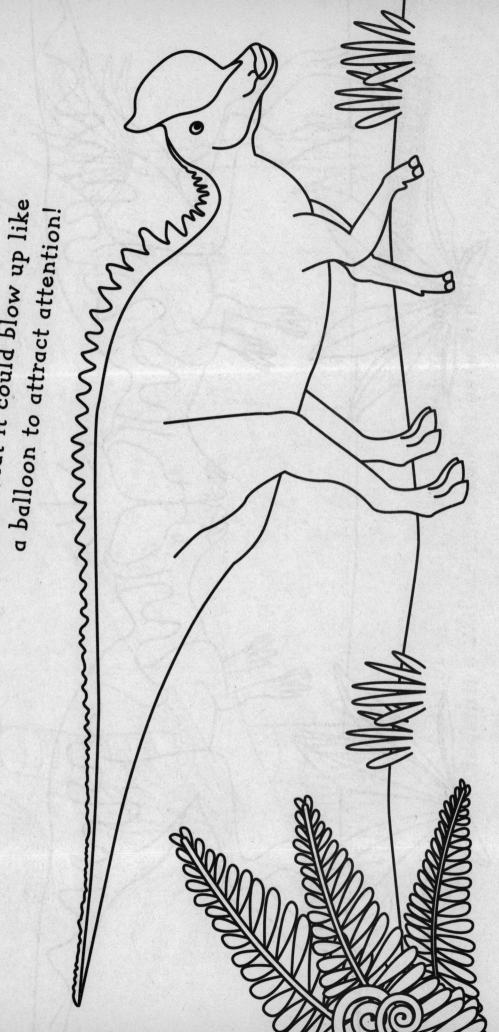

Saurolophus had a pouch on its head that it could blow up like a balloon to attract attention!

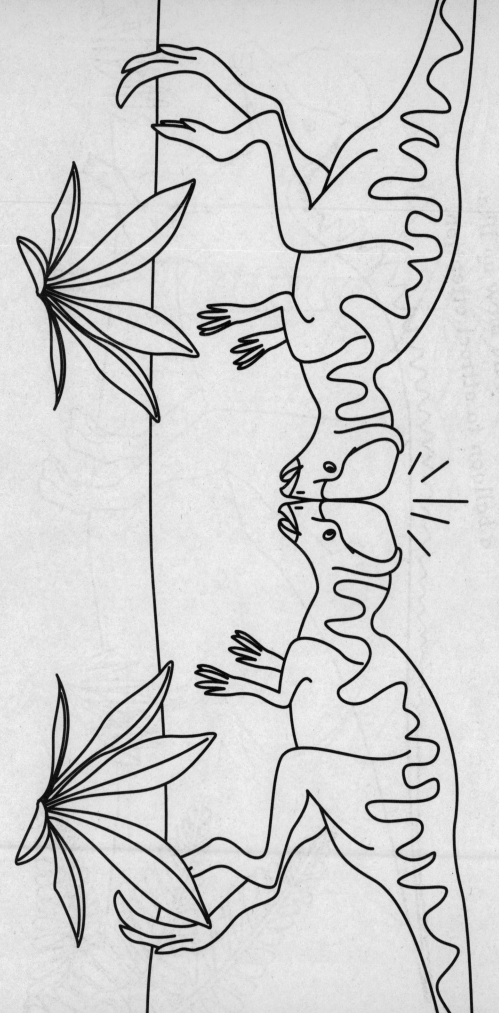

Stegoceras had a thick skull that it probably used in "head-butting" battles.

Pachycephalosaurus had a bony dome on top of its skull that was over 9 inches thick!

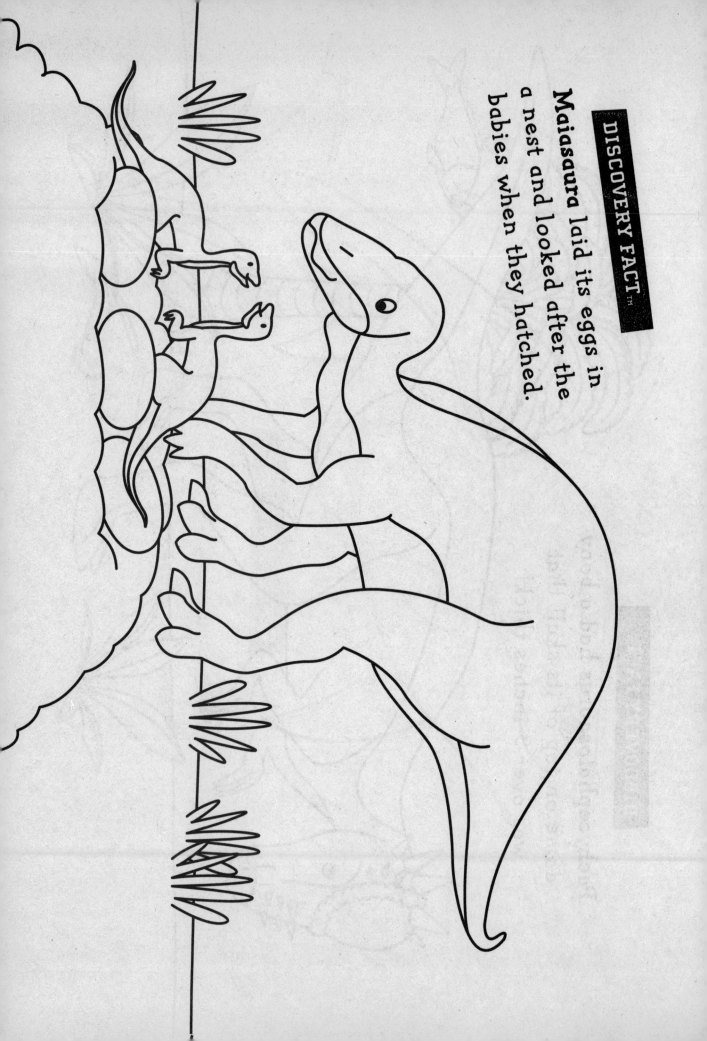

Maiasaura laid its eggs in
a nest and looked after the
babies when they hatched.

DISCOVERY FACT™

Ichthyosaurs were great swimmers and looked like dolphins—just much bigger!

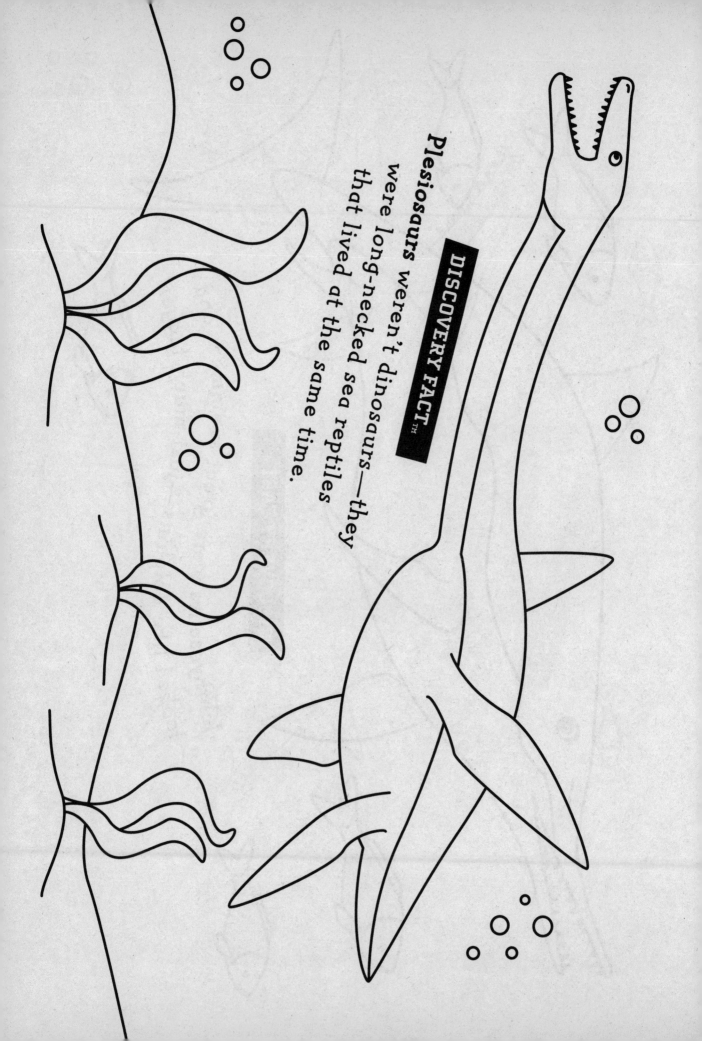

DISCOVERY FACT™

Plesiosaurs weren't dinosaurs—they were long-necked sea reptiles that lived at the same time.

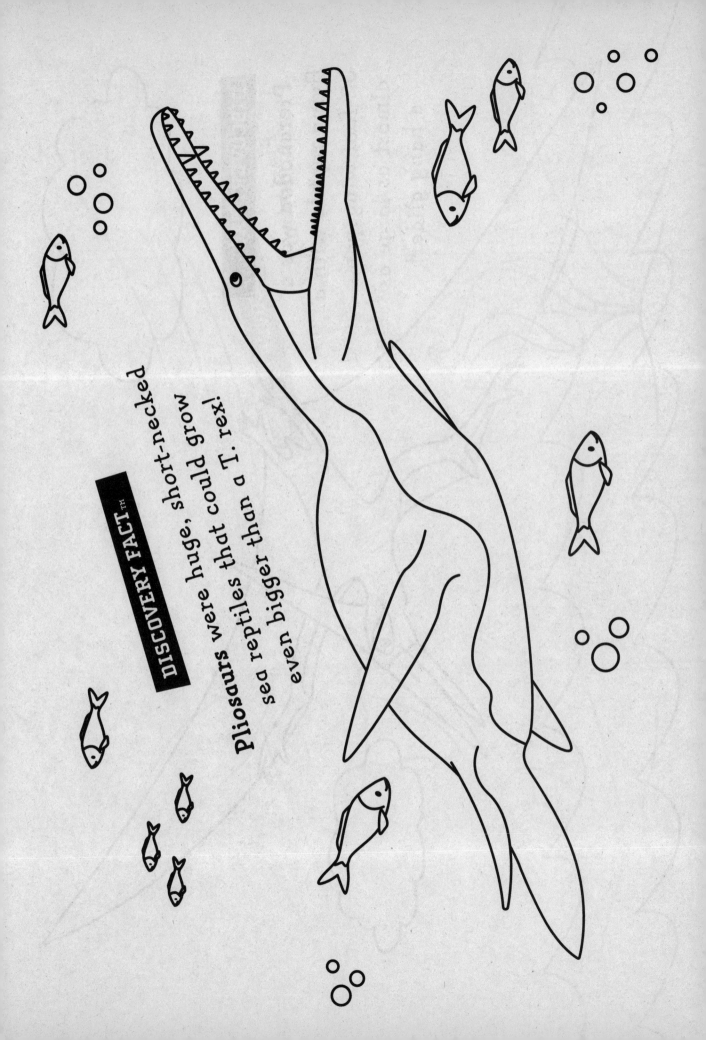

DISCOVERY FACT™

Pliosaurs were huge, short-necked sea reptiles that could grow even bigger than a T. rex!

DISCOVERY FACT™

Pteranodon was a flying reptile with a 32-foot wingspan—almost as large as a hang glider!

DISCOVERY FACT™

Archaeopteryx is the earliest known flying bird!

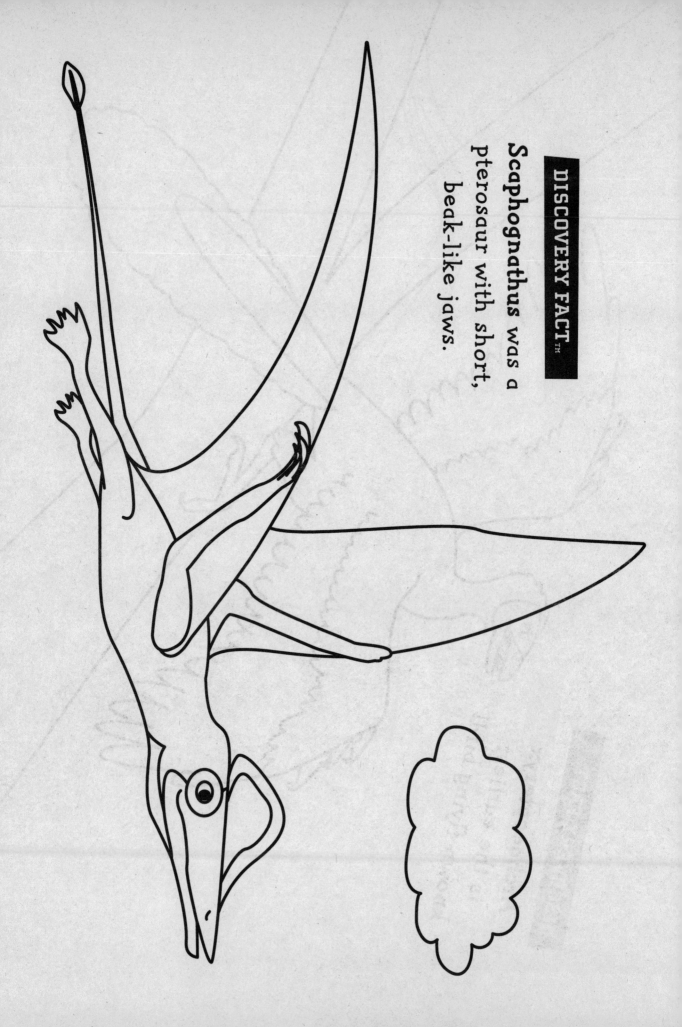

Scaphognathus was a pterosaur with short, beak-like jaws.

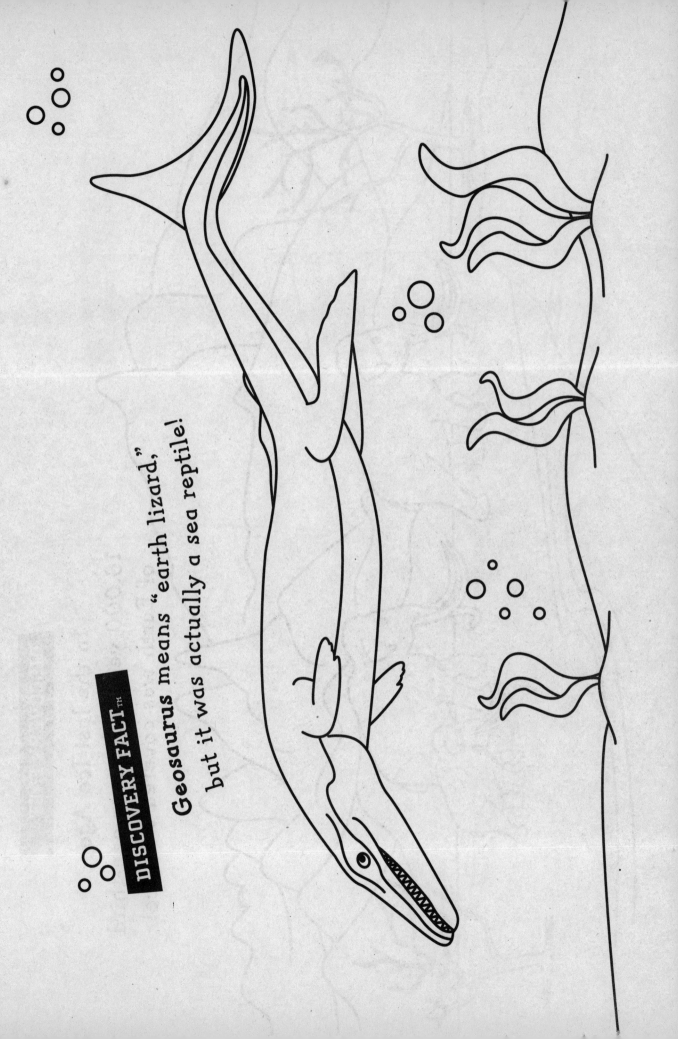

DISCOVERY FACT™

Geosaurus means "earth lizard," but it was actually a sea reptile!

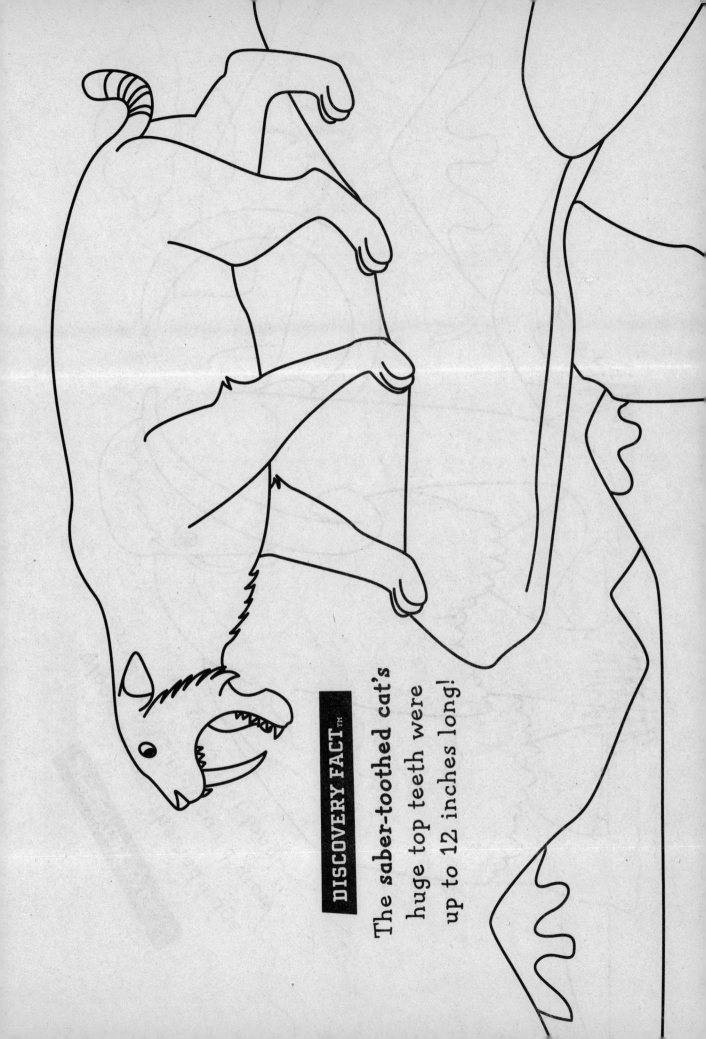

DISCOVERY FACT™

The saber-toothed cat's huge top teeth were up to 12 inches long!

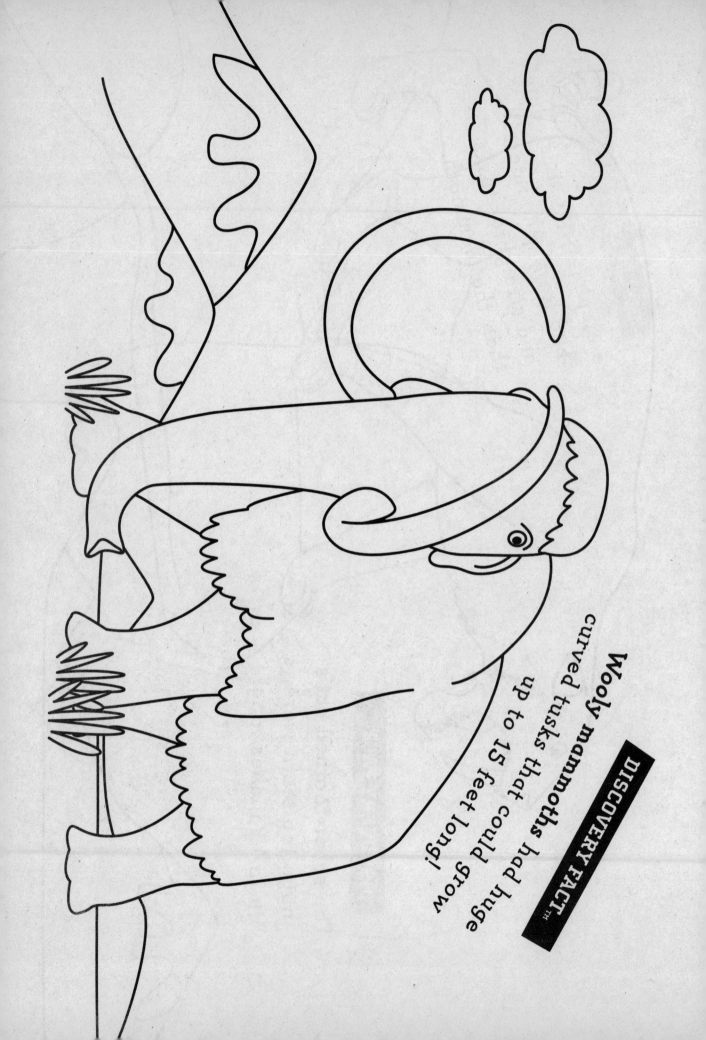

Wooly mammoths had huge curved tusks that could grow up to 15 feet long!

DISCOVERY FACT™

The elephant-like mastodon had lower shoulders and straighter tusks than the mammoth.

The **ground sloth** looked a little like a hamster, but it was as big as an elephant!

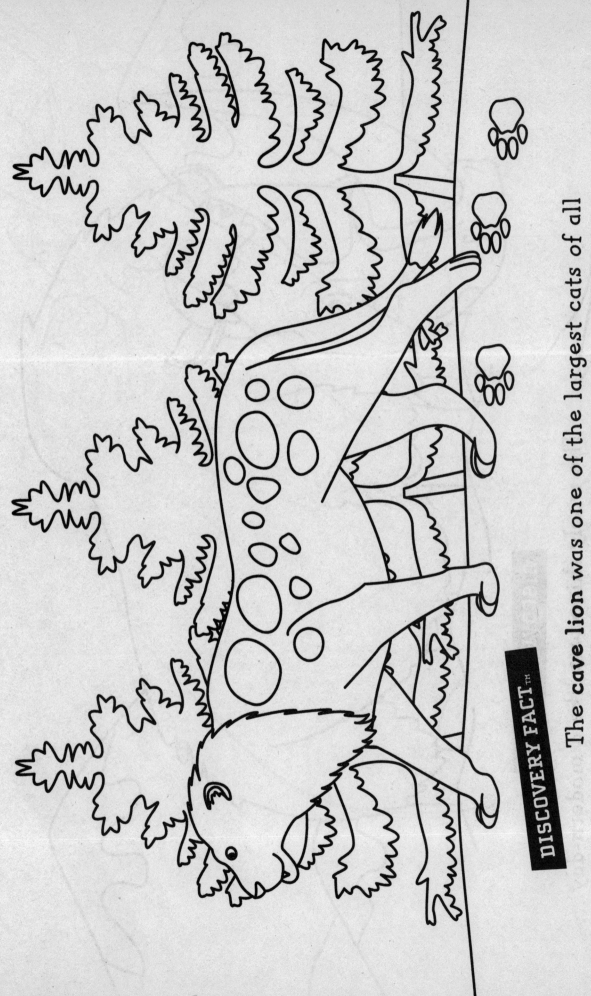

DISCOVERY FACT™ The cave lion was one of the largest cats of all time—even bigger than today's biggest lion!

The **wooly rhino** was like a modern-day rhinoceros, but with shaggy fur to keep it warm.

DISCOVERY FACT™

Daeodon looked like a wild pig, but it grew to the size of a hippo!

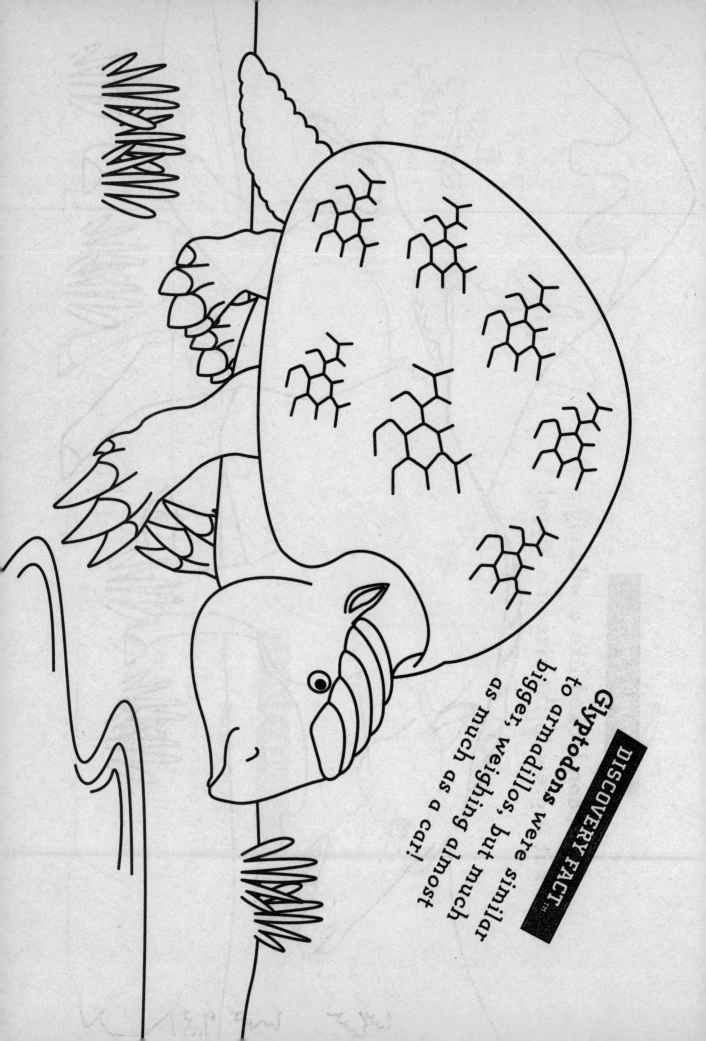

Glyptodons were similar to armadillos, but much bigger, weighing almost as much as a car!

DISCOVERY FACT™

DISCOVERY FACT™

Megaloceros was a giant deer—a tall man standing beside it would only reach its neck!

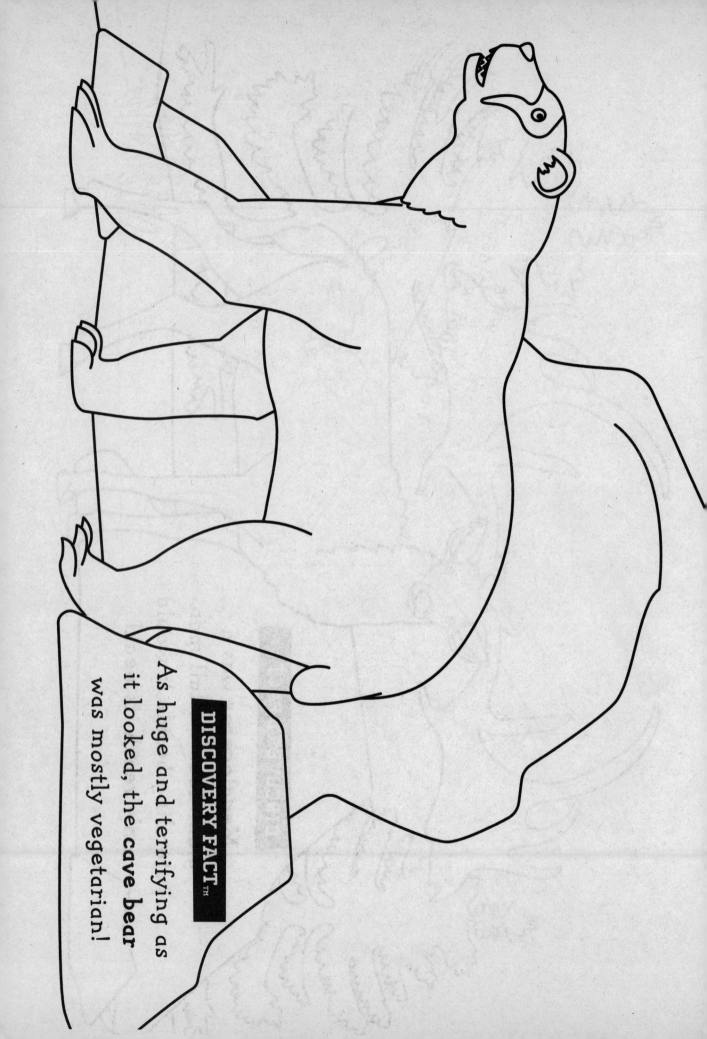

DISCOVERY FACT™

As huge and terrifying as it looked, the **cave bear** was mostly vegetarian!

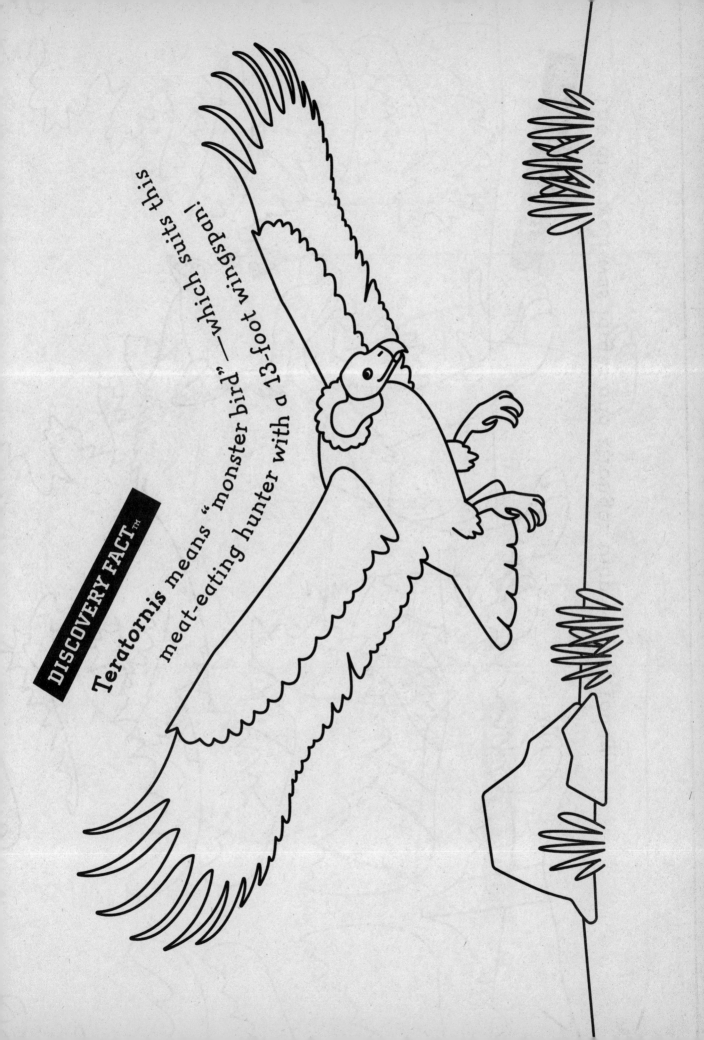

DISCOVERY FACT™

Teratornis means "monster bird"—which suits this meat-eating hunter with a 13-foot wingspan!

The **dire wolf** was larger and stronger than wolves today.

DISCOVERY FACT™

The short-faced bear was probably the fastest running bear that ever lived!

DISCOVERY FACT ™

Dodos became extinct less than 100 years after coming into contact with humans!